Textiles and new technology: 2010

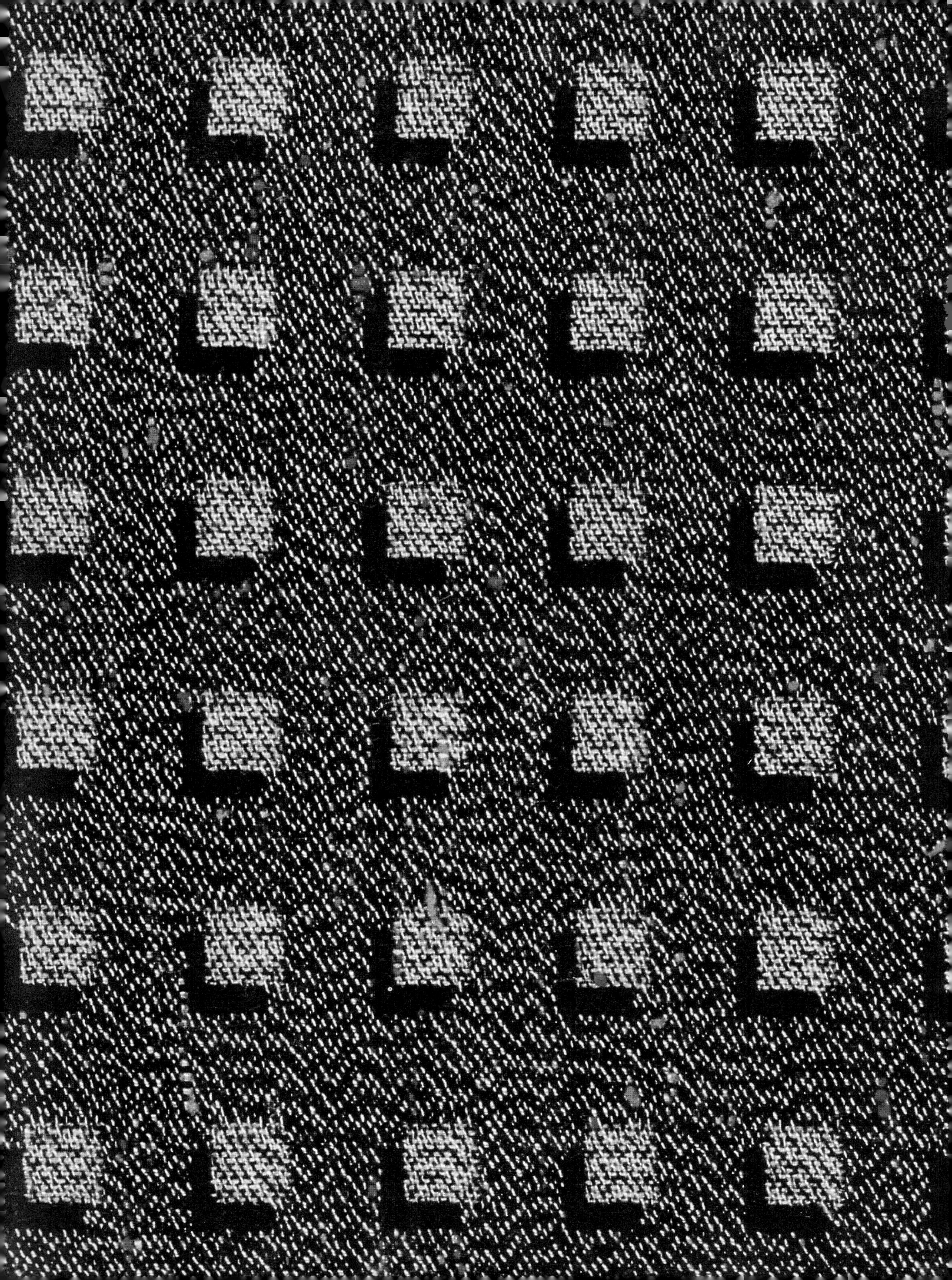

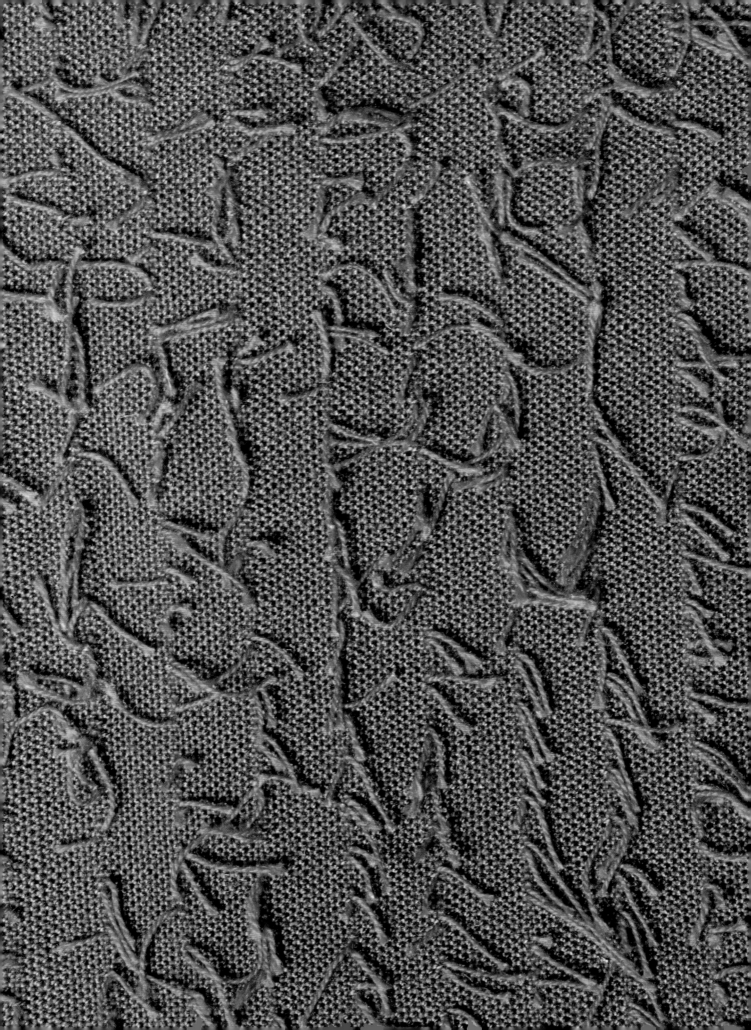

Artemis London

Textiles and new technology: 2010

Edited by Sarah Braddock and Marie O'Mahony

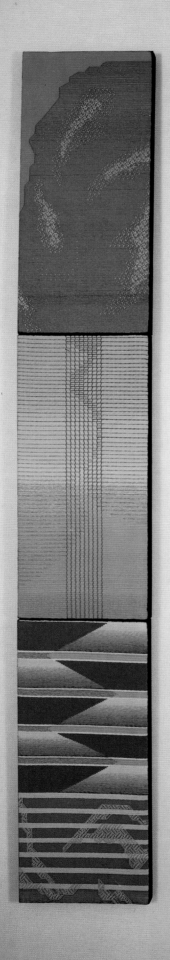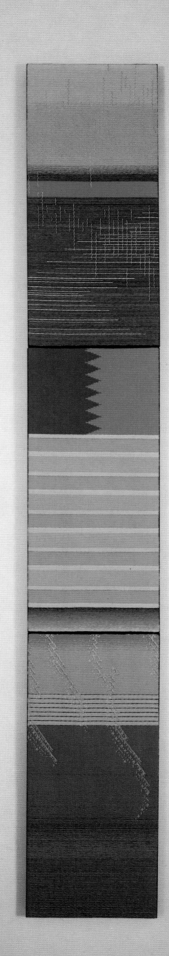

Contents

Preface

This book looks at the dramatic effect new technologies are having on textiles, illustrating the current advances while adopting a forward-looking outlook. The concept is to document work by textile artists and designers who are fusing new technology with traditional textile materials and techniques. Far from being overwhelmed by modern technology, they are placing it in a larger context, understanding its value in yielding innovative results and expanding the media of textiles. The book came about through research undertaken towards the Craft's Council exhibition, 2010, and the essays here discuss certain issues raised by the exhibition.

From Japan to Latvia, current investigation into the development of synthetic/natural components and computer-aided design/manufacture, coupled with an understanding of the broader nature of textiles, is promoting a new aesthetic. Barriers are broken down when technology overthrows preconceptions by providing cloth as strong as steel and metallised fabrics as soft as silk. Research into flexible structures by architectural engineers is one area where sophisticated textiles are being developed for building. Industrial materials and techniques previously developed for completely different purposes are being utilised and expanded by textile artists and designers. The continuing concern for the environment claims the interest of those working with protective, recycled and responsive materials. Work shown in *Textiles and New Technology* covers the disciplines of art, craft, design, architecture, fashion, science and engineering which frequently cross-refer. Their relative ideologies and methodologies are examined here by writers from diverse backgrounds including curators, lecturers and journalists.

It is hoped that *Textiles and New Technology* will provide an insight into this exciting time for textiles which simultaneously embraces the past and the present, and optimistically looks to the future.

Sarah Braddock and Marie O'Mahony
Curators of 2010

Respect for tradition, curiosity for technology

Sarah Braddock

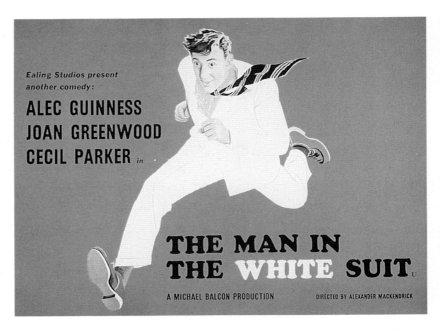

Ealing Studios present another comedy:

ALEC GUINNESS
JOAN GREENWOOD
CECIL PARKER in

THE MAN IN
THE WHITE SUIT U

A MICHAEL BALCON PRODUCTION   DIRECTED BY ALEXANDER MACKENDRICK

Poster for 'The Man in the White Suit'
1951, Ealing Studios Ltd,
Warner Bros.
This Ealing comedy
demonstrates the failure of new
technology when it is used
without regard for tradition and
the historical context.
© BFI Stills, Posters and Designs

As we approach the close of the twentieth century the unification of ancient craft and new technology has an important role to play in creating a more harmonious environment. Textiles are one of the earliest creative media; the ancient technique of weaving is found in many cultures and has changed little. Traditional processes can be given new meaning and value by modern technology, which will expand the role of textiles. Textile artists and designers world-wide are looking to the latest technology and recent developments to bring new life and fresh meaning to their craft. Some use traditional materials combined with new manufacturing technologies, others work with sophisticated textile materials and ancient techniques. In both cases it is the union of tradition and technology that will yield innovative results and provide a new aesthetic.

The strength of much of Japanese textile art and design lies in this combination of tradition and high technology. The work is both primitive and avant-garde, fully integrating the old with contemporary society. Junichi Arai, textile designer for the manufacturing company Nuno, started by weaving textiles for kimonos in his father's factory in Kiryu, Japan. (Kiryu is famous for its tradition of Jacquard weaving.) Junichi Arai developed an understanding of textiles from an early age and uses this knowledge to subvert techniques and create unique fabrics. He fuses the past, present and future, combining time-honoured Japanese textile traditions with the latest advances in computer technology and manufacturing advances to create fabrics that are evocative of the past and yet totally modern. 'It is nonsense to ignore the potential of computers and high-tech materials in this age', says Junichi Arai. He has computerised part of the Jacquard weaving process to produce multi-layered fabrics with a wide range of constructions.

Reiko Sudo, textile designer and director of Nuno, utilises techniques usually reserved for industrial application, and computers both enhance and transform her textile designs, producing beautiful results. Both Junichi Arai and Reiko Sudo gain inspiration from the philosophy and technical skills of many cultural traditions, including their own.

The work of Japanese fashion designer Issey Miyake advances beyond conventional boundaries, combining both eastern and western ideologies. He follows a national tradition of reverence for the kimono by cutting into the cloth as little as possible, and combines this with western attitudes to dress, creating a new aesthetic. In close collaboration with his textile

Issey Miyake
Nylon dress
This sculptural garment is
made of iridescent nylon which
has been moulded by heat. The
shape is achieved by forming
without cutting or sewing.
© *Marie Claire (spring/summer
1991)*
Photograph by Keiichi Tahara

Patrice Hugues
'L'Entredeux', 1992 (detail)
Thermo-printed polyester
H 250 cm W 120 cm (per unit)
Patrice Hugues' textile artwork
explores layer upon layer of
printed fabric and illustrates
the inherent qualities of
flexibility and fluidity that
textiles possess. As the viewer
passes near the work the
separate pieces flutter with the
movement of the air.
© *Alain Oudin, Paris*

designer, Makiko Minagawa, he revives, reasserts
and extends traditional Japanese techniques
such as shibori[1] in making new fabrics. Issey
Miyake and Makiko Minagawa use craft tradition
but believe that the way forward is to combine
this with sophisticated technology. 'Tradition
exists only as a way of linking the past to the
present' according to Issey Miyake.[2] Between
them they have invented pioneering methods of
fabric construction such as concurrently cutting
and bonding thermoplastic fabrics with an
electric charge, a technique usually used for
steel.[3] They have also experimented with highly-
developed synthetics. Ancient traditions are
combined with modern industrial methods to
produce contemporary as well as futuristic
fabrics and garments.

In the development of new materials, both
designers and scientists have looked towards
composites.[4] Composite yarns are being
developed with synthetics, carbon, glass and
metals to be used in two- and three-dimensional
constructions. British textile designer Nigel
Marshall has been researching composites and
plastics for many years and has produced a
variety of surfaces and structures. He combines
strips of sheet film with monofilament and
metallic yarns to make textiles using traditional
techniques of weaving and knitting. The

configuration of these textiles is then altered by subjecting them to treatments such as laminating, heat-bonding, vacuum-forming and heat-transfer printing. Lamination provides increased physical strength while allowing varied decorative effects. This has led him to explore possible collaborations with producers of protective clothing.

Research into alternative fabrics provides the starting point for Crissij van den Munckhof, a designer working in Britain. She uses a material called Felvet, a composite fabric of polyurethane and nylon which has a texture between that of felt and velvet and markets her work as 'one hundred per cent unnatural'. The technique used is based on felting, the most ancient way of creating a fabric by bonding fibres. Felvet is the outcome of much research and development with textile manufacturers, resulting in a textile which is strong, light, retains its shape and is capable of being sculpted. Textiles, by their nature, are semi-finished, and components in the art and design process. Crissij van den Munckhof fully explores the thermoplastic properties of synthetics, allowing her to create dramatic hat designs.

Contemporary textile artists and designers enhance the rich mixture of tradition and technology by exploring the tensions between the natural and urban worlds, and between natural and synthetic materials. Many Japanese artists and designers are inspired by nature. This is apparent in their aesthetic tradition which underpins much of the imagery and the materials they use. This respect for nature combined with sophisticated technologies creates a unique tension. Issey Miyake's and Makiko Minagawa's love of the natural world and organic materials finds its expression in their curiosity about synthetic materials and processes.

American textile artist Warren Seelig is inspired by the urban environment in his sculptural textile work, and uses forms developed from modern architecture as his visual source. To emphasise this interest he employs industrial materials and methodologies to create abstract forms. He has been absorbed by the relationship between skeleton and skin for some time; tensile membranes look back to the earliest shelter constructions, nomadic tents. Seelig employs lightweight materials in his structures and uses a recently developed fabric, Tyvek, in combination with stainless steel.[5] He exploits this textile's inherent properties of strength and minimal weight to create pliable surfaces which are tensioned between stainless steel axles, allowing the materials to be inter-dependent.

The work of the French textile artist Patrice

Pēteris Sidars
'The Sun'
Woven fibre optic
H 185 cm W 125 cm D 40 cm
The fibre ends of 'The Sun' are visible in this woven textile artwork, rolled to make the best of the reflective qualities of this material.
Sponsor: Lattelekom
(Tilts Communications)

Interior of Nomad restaurant, Tokyo

Architect Toyo Ito, fabric by Reiko Sudo

Nomad, a restaurant in the Roppongi district of Tokyo, was designed by Toyo Ito, a Japanese architect renowned for his adventurous projects. Reiko Sudo constructed fabric installations for the interior. These are suspended from the ceiling, echoing its aluminium sheet cladding. Her aim was to integrate the fabric and architecture and towards this she chose to work with polyester fabric, finely spattered with aluminium, which was slit and then woven. The result is a beautiful, open, reflective surface which changes the atmosphere of the interior.
© Nuno Corporation

Hugues shows layers of information assembled to create a new reality. The artist makes reference to the urban environment, illustrating visual chaos by exploring pattern and image, incorporating the printed word on fabric. Using high-technology heat-transfer printing techniques on silk organza, a transparent and fluid textile, the meaning of the words loses clarity when the fabric moves in a breeze, the words themselves becoming abstract visual marks. The multi-layered nature of the work enables Patrice Hugues to vary the arrangement and to orchestrate different effects.

Pēteris Sidars is a textile artist who employs high-technology fibre optics, a medium principally used by the communications industry, as well as in science and medicine. The idea of transmitting and guiding light from a source using fibre is not a recent invention but current research has made further developments possible. Pēteris Sidars manipulates the material, slitting the fibre with a special diamond knife, a complicated and labour-intensive process, so that it will reflect light. At his workshop in Kuldiga, Latvia, craftspeople help to weave fibre-optic strands with synthetic yarns on traditional looms. Once removed from the loom, the piece is rolled to maximise the effect of light being emitted, resulting in a work which under different lighting conditions is both

mysterious and dramatic.

The sculptural, heavily textured fabrics of Nuno are often reliant on a mixture of natural and synthetic yarns. Both Junichi Arai and Reiko Sudo explore unlikely combinations of natural and synthetic fibres at every stage from yarn to finishing process; sometimes exposing the fabrics to extreme temperatures, causing the synthetic components to blister and shrink. The fabrics are layered and sculpted using many different techniques; minimal use of colour draws attention to texture and structure. All woven textiles rely on a certain amount of tension but the fabrics designed for Nuno upset the balance, giving unpredictable effects. Junichi Arai uses new technology to create fabrics that have wonderful textural surfaces. He starts by designing with the yarns, handling them and being inspired by touch. He then works from the computer to the loom creating sculptural, sophisticated fabrics instead of graphically plotting the designs. Both Junichi Arai and Reiko Sudo exploit the qualities of the textiles by observing different characters of the yarns used and continuously exploring new manufacturing techniques. They respond to the inherent qualities of the chosen materials, building them up as an architect or an engineer might. Reiko Sudo has furthered this idea and has collaborated with the Japanese architect Toyo Ito on adventurous projects treating textiles as a construction material.

Most synthetics began their lives by simulating the look and feel of natural fibres. Today, with new attitudes and advanced technology we are able to refine, re-work and constantly improve textiles so that they have a new integrity of their own. The development of micro-fibres has allowed textiles a totally new range of characteristics. Micro-fibres are extremely fine and capable of being engineered to specification. Japan leads in the development of these fibres, using advanced technology such as chemical research and computer-aided design and manufacture. Kuraray, a textile company which began by making 'artificial silk', now uses innovative technology and research to create textiles for the twenty-first century. This company is developing many high function textiles, such as quick-drying yarns, water-absorbing yarns and even yarns capable of converting solar rays into heat energy. In Japan, where textiles is a growing industry, research is considered vital and such developments are happening fast. Japan has pumped money into its textile industry for many decades, combining a strong textile craft tradition with new technology.

Following the sophistication of micro-fibres,

Film still from 'Until the End of the World' by Wim Wenders
Solveig Dommartin as Claire Townew, an image set in 1999. Travel between the major world cities is unimaginably fast. But the high-tech society sadly lacks something undefinable and the characters portrayed have no roots in this transient world.
© BFI Stills, Posters and Designs

even more dramatic developments are expected for this last decade of the millennium.[6] Fabrics are now being developed which can be programmed to adapt to various conditions and react to the environment. These 'smart' fabrics will possess all the qualities traditionally required in a fabric and others not anticipated. Advanced research by large companies will eventually filter down to be readily available. Artists and designers using the new textiles will eventually expand their capabilities and stimulate further research. In these ways both large textile companies and individual textile artists and designers can influence each other.

As we go into the twenty-first century, artists and designers understand that a balance between high technology and tradition is imperative. In trying to comprehend the past, present and future in this rapidly changing world they are developing a sensitivity to their own cultural values and those of others. They recognise the need for harmonious relationships between humankind, the natural world and the increasingly complex urban, computer-age environment . As Junichi Arai says, 'What use is high technology if we do not know the soul of the craft?'[7]

1. Shibori is an ancient technique of tie-dye resist. The fabric is bound, tied, stitched, crumpled, folded or pleated to prevent certain areas from absorbing colour.
2. Lecture by Issey Miyake at the Domus Academy, Milan, June 1986.
3. Most synthetics are thermoplastic which means that above a certain temperature the structure breaks down, becomes fluid and is capable of being re-shaped.
4. A composite is a material made of different components integrated at various stages of the production process and is used for everyday products, architecture and advanced space exploration.
5. Tyvek or 'envelope paper' is manufactured by DuPont Corporation and is a spun bonded olefin fibre derived from high-density polyethylene fibres. The fibres are bonded by heat and pressure to create a translucent, strong, smooth fabric.

6. According to 'The Synthetic Fibre Industry for the Twenty-First Century', this industry will be a 'life-culture-creative-industry' in the next century. From *Knitting International*, London, June 1992
7. From the exhibition catalogue *Hand and Technology*, August 1992.

Scanning the inner fabric

Sandy Black

The impact of new technology on every aspect of our daily lives can hardly be overstated. Its growth over the past decade has transformed both our working practices and our leisure activities in ways we have yet to fully comprehend.

The benefits of computer technology for design and production – its ability to handle complex tasks, speed, cost-saving – have long been recognised and utilised in many fields from aerospace and automotive engineering to architecture and product design. However, it was the introduction of colour painting and drawing systems in the late seventies which was the catalyst for change in the graphic design profession and, more recently, the textiles and fashion industries.

In the textiles industry, as in many others, the technological revolution has transformed production processes; the ability to integrate design into computer-controlled systems has forced designers to rethink their approach to designing, and managers to rethink the role and position of design within company structures. The introduction of computer-aided design and manufacture – known as CAD/CAM – has opened up new opportunities which have yet to be fully explored. In the new computer-integrated manufacturing (CIM) the product and its design information are repositioned centrally within the organisation; design has so often in the past been regarded as a peripheral activity.

As large textiles and fashion companies have begun to invest in the new technology, design has become the focus of attention. From tentative beginnings a few years ago, new highly sophisticated software tools have been developed, showing the benefits of recent collaborations between programmers and designer-users. Textile designers have had to change from traditional manual working methods with brush and paints, pens and point paper, to new and alien computer workstations; their environment has changed from a noisy but inspiring clutter to a sterile grey box. However, new devices for freehand drawing such as the pressure-sensitive stylus and digitising tablet are replacing the clumsier keyboard and mouse, and the introduction of the scanner has opened up the completely new area of computer imaging; almost anything can become the basis of a design once it is captured in digital format inside the machine. The computer is certainly the ultimate tool of image manipulation, as current films and advertising testify.

As the technology has evolved and prices have fallen, access to CAD has broadened, allowing smaller design companies and individuals to experiment with software based on the personal

Patricia Kinsella
'La Pergola', 1991 (detail)
Cotton yarns mounted on wooden frames
Each square 61 x 61 cm
H 132 cm W 203 cm
Patricia Kinsella works with a computer loom to create intricate woven structures made up of separate modules capable of being rearranged into different structures. In 'La Pergola' the vivid patterns are inspired by the formal language of the weaving process.
© The Collection of LongHouse Foundation
Photograph by Alessandro Pianti

Ceri Isaac
'Word Debris', 1993
Design for printed fabric,
Athena scan collaged and
manipulated
© *Athena Design Systems*

computer. Individual designers and artists are also able to access new technology through CAD bureaux or industry collaborations which are increasingly being established.

The changes that are taking place have forced a re-examination of the creative design process itself and there is a new excitement emerging as designers and artists are coming to terms with the new technology, and using it to explore some of the fundamental questions raised about ideas, process, technique, tools and media.

In this transitional phase, the potential of CAD/CAM is just beginning to be explored. Computer technology has generated a variety of reactions from designers and artists: it is viewed by some as a threat to traditional disciplines in art and design; by others as a box of tricks, a tool kit for easier, faster solutions to old problems; by yet others as a vehicle for untold experimentation. New tools need not be easy to use – just difficult enough to stimulate creative thought. The most innovative work results from an open-minded and experimental approach to the new medium, allowing the use of the computer to lead to results otherwise unobtainable and probably unforeseen. Existing boundaries and preconceptions must be broken down in order to allow new developments, and those working outside the constraints of

Philippa M Brock
Computer visualisation of
seating unit, 1993
Woven fabric designed on
Apple Macintosh, texture
mapped to show effect

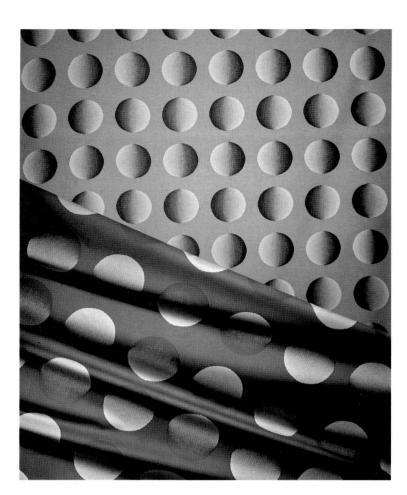

Vibeke Riisberg
'Reflektion', 1992
Cotton sation, designed on a
Mac II and hand printed,
manufactured by Kvadrat
L 320 cm W 140 cm D 10 cm
© Photographer Ole Akhoj/
maker/Kavdrat

commercial environments may be best placed to achieve new results.

The use of computers in textile design within industry is now established, but not yet exploited for its true creative potential. The major areas of printed, knitted and woven textiles are at different stages of development within CAD/CAM. Weaving has a long established connection to the evolution of the computer, and now computer-assisted weaving has freed time previously spent on laborious processes for more creative work, benefitting both large- and small-scale users. Although CAD for knitted textiles is very advanced in the design and production of colour and stitch patterns for commercial knitwear design, access to production equipment by individuals is difficult outside industry or education. There remains a wide division between small CAD systems and machines for studio use, and large industrial CAD/CAM systems, but a great deal of interesting work is being achieved by manual methods.

Printed textile designer/artists have begun to use computer generated imagery for the basis of their print ideas, using the unique power of the computer for image manipulation. Original (or copied!) artwork, photographs and objects can be scanned in and combined with work generated on the screen and endlessly varied to create collages of texture, line and image. In industry this can be an all too easy method of producing fast but poor quality designs based only on computer tricks: responsibility for the integrity of the design still rests on the skills and experience of the designer.

Accurate colour reproduction from computer screen to paper and fabric is of great importance to printed textiles, and has taken much research to perfect, which has delayed the general acceptance of CAD for print design. The design-led Italian printed textiles company Ratti have developed their own integrated CAD/CAM system to match precisely the needs of their high fashion quality design for print production. The latest (third generation) computer software tools for print design are at last capturing the imagination of designers. One such, the Athena Design System, has just been launched with the aim of providing a natural and intuitive tool for creative working, developed with designers and artists for both small and large users. The scanning facility has been perfected to a high degree, with which multiple layers of images can be built up, and the system allows the individuality of the designer to be clearly expressed.

The scope of textiles for furnishings and interiors has been greatly extended by CAD/CAM developments, for example allowing large-scale designs to be achieved with comparative ease. The printed fabric design exhibited by Jonathan Fuller has been generated and manipulated on computer but realised in the traditional manner by hand screen printing. The textures captured by scanning have been enlarged, exposing each pixel (picture element) of the image in great detail. Vibeke Riisberg uses the power of both repetition and scale within her work, starting from a computer generated image which is enhanced to explore a theme of light and illusory dimensionality in the printed fabric. A similar theme of graphic illusion is woven into the structure of Bobbi Shortlidge's *Woven Bands Series* with the aid of a computerised loom.

Anne Mieke Kooper designs woven pile fabrics for upholstery which have highly structured surfaces. Whether working within industry or on personal pieces, she likes to extend boundaries, and challenge the limitations of the industrial process, and of our perceptions. The fabrics in the exhibition are her most recent experiments in CAD/CAM. She says: 'When it is upholstery it should be possible to sit on it – if the feeling is strange or people do not dare to sit on it I think it is great, because it means that people react to it.'

The notion of functionality is one area where artists and designers begin to diverge – the designer is always constrained to some extent by the end use of the product (although the need to meet requirements can itself force creative solutions). In the opinion of Vibeke Vestby, lecturer, weaver and CAD/CAM expert, 'textiles were always made as a compromise between function and ornamentation', and industrial textile production has freed the textile artist to use qualities of fabric construction 'for purposes dictated by pure artistic and aesthetic concepts.' To this end, she has developed a software package specifically for hand weavers using computerised looms which allows complete design freedom by selection and control of each individual thread to 'focus on the unexplored possibilities of the architecture of interlacing.'

Some of the most inspiring work can be found where older craft-based skills meet new technology, not just through the computer screen (which in itself imposes hidden constraints), but in conjunction with new production methods combined with 'hands on' techniques. Artist Emily DuBois is deeply influenced by Taoist philosophy, and uses computer-aided weaving to create her work with a combination of traditional techniques including ikat and Japanese shibori resist dyeing, thus creating and imbueing the fabric with multiple layers of both process and interpretation. *Fragment* is one of a series of works inspired by patterns in nature, and which

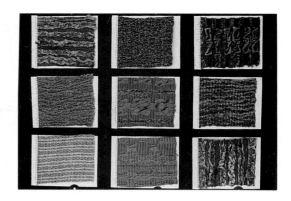

Karen Rolfe
Three-dimensional jersey-knit samples, 1993
Wool and synthetics using Moratronic CAD/CAM system
L 38 cm W 15 cm
Photograph by Karen Rolfe

beautifully express the dualism between uncompromising computer-designed weave structures and the unpredictable dyeing processes. Textile designer Karen Rolfe recently graduated from the Royal College of Art in London where she designed knitted jersey fashion fabrics with complex three dimensional knit structures, effectively combining CAD/CAM technology with hand finishing and printing techniques to create distressed and aged qualities which are not obviously knitted.

The meeting of the artist with the computer is fascinating to observe. The computer environment is a modern cross-roads for the two cultures, scientific/technological and artistic/ creative, which have since the Renaissance become separated. A convergence of disciplines is now made possible by the underlying structure of computer technology, bringing together artists, designers, mathematicians, computer programmers, production technologists and industrialists. This is not the first time that artists have worked with computers; during the sixties and seventies the ideas of artificial intelligence inspired such artists as Harold Cohen (see page 59) to produce computer-drawn artworks based on complex series of mathematical instructions and rules. It is interesting to note that during this phase of computer evolution (before the

Alexander McQueen
Jacket, autumn 1994 collection
Jacket fabric with
deconstructed images
handprinted by Wilson and
Brennan
Photograph by Anni Phillips

graphical screen interface), the experimental use of the computer was the province of the artist rather than the designer.

Both textile artists and textile designers are using CAD as a production tool for weaving, and some have access to design systems. One artist, Cynthia Schira, participated in the Art and Industry Jacquard weaving project, resulting in her work *Repeated Homage*. This forward-thinking project, undertaken in 1991 at the Müller-Zell weaving factory in Germany was devised to 'set artistic standards for the electronic revolution in Jacquard weaving' (previously a time-consuming and very costly mechanical process), and gave several textile artists access to the latest CAD/CAM facilities. Cynthia Schira's aim was to produce 'atypical' Jacquards and to avoid being too seduced by technique she worked in black and white. In contrast, Patricia Kinsella, another participant in the project, made dramatic use of scale and pattern in boldly patterned, colourful complex weaves.

For all weavers there is a common quest for fabric with integrity and inherent qualities which might be threatened by the process of designing and weaving through a computer screen. In using CAD for textiles, it is vital that the artist/designer/operator has a sound knowledge of fabric qualities – despite their impressive

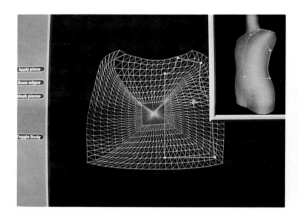

CIMTEX
Virtual catwalk, 1994
© *Dr Gary Fozzard/De Montford University*

Emma Nixey
Sculptured Lycra knitwear,
1992
Produced using CAD/CAM
system at the University of
Brighton
Photograph by Bob Seago

capabilities for visualisation and simulation, CAD systems cannot (yet) substitute for tactile sensation, which is as important in textile design as visual qualities.

In the textiles and fashion industry, many CAD systems are used primarily for presentation and sales rather than design. Visualisation and simulation of fabrics on paper and on a photographic model have become an important communication tool, but often at the expense of design creativity. The most widely used systems are based on designing in two dimensions, with the third dimension visualised by complex body-mapping processes. Fashion design in three dimensions, taking into account fabric drape and handle, is the subject of much current research, notably by Stephen Gray of Nottingham Trent University, and the CIMTEX project at De Montfort University, led by Dr Gary Fozzard. A major part of these projects concerns modelling on virtual bodies within the computer, and Stephen Gray's team is creating its own 'virtual catwalk' show. Fashion design is a fast moving business, and the competitive advantages which can be gained with CAD/CAM are eagerly sought. The main challenge for fashion CAD is the translation of an often intuitive approach to designing, which moves freely between two and three dimensions, with constant modifications being made.

Computer-aided design is here to stay and we must embrace the challenge. At its worst, CAD overwhelms and dazzles the user, who can easily produce banal work. At its best, the use of CAD frees the designer for greater experimentation. The use of the technology should be transparent, providing a means to access the underlying design and structural potential through the processes of creating, testing and selecting, but it should not be an end in itself. It is all too easy to be seduced by the powers of a CAD system and to be led astray by its wealth of techniques – the artist's/designer's vision must remain intact. However, in exploring a new medium, it is vital to retain a balance between fixed ideas and spontaneous outcomes which lead off in new directions. Many artists and designers thrive on the 'accidental' and the computer can initially seem restrictive to serendipity – everything is contained within its world – but that remains to be challenged. If the computer is used as a tool for the mind and not just the hand; not to replace existing practices, but to add to them; perhaps to synthesise a new visual and tactile language, rather than repeat what we already understand – then who knows what will happen?

Across the divide

Martina Margetts

In homes, a haunted apparatus sleeps,
that snores when you pick it up.

If the ghost cries they carry it
to their lips and soothe it to sleep

with sounds. And yet, they wake it up
deliberately, by tickling with a finger.

This description of a telephone appears in Craig Raine's poem, *A Martian Sends a Postcard Home*, published fifteen years ago. The so-called Martian poetry of that time viewed the familiar world from a quizzical, unfamiliar standpoint. This was typical of the 1960s and seventies, when established canons were dislodged. Duchamp's gauntlet had been taken up in all creative fields, including textiles which reassessed form and function through an investigation of materials, techniques, scale, subject matter and context.

The revisionist climate of Postmodernism encouraged interdisciplinary debate and activity. Anthropologists discussed design, scientists pronounced on religion and computers made art. In art schools and then in the professional milieu, industrial designers and sculptors, architects and fashion designers, performance artists and jewellers shared ideas and projects. This creative and intellectual fluidity, underscored by social, economic and technological change, provides the context for creative professionals today who work 'across the divide'.

Maria Blaisse, Kyoko Kumai, Andrea Burkhard and Karina Holmes (from Holland, Japan, Switzerland and Britain respectively) have trained in textiles and developed their work in the direction of architecture and interior design, dance, fashion and industrial innovation, while Ron Arad, Tom Dixon and the partnerships of Ove Arup with Michael Hopkins and D Y Davies with Atelier One (all British-based) have developed the vocabulary of furniture design and architecture through the application of new fabrics. All of them share an interest in exploring textiles and their processes, to develop the languages of art and design.

A fundamental exploration of textile is the purpose of Maria Blaisse's recent work with students at Kassel University in Germany. Their startling pleated or honeycombed heat-treated materials, which evoke nature's lava flows, seas and rock strata, indicate some of the possibilities regarding textiles' structure and form. The experiments also reveal textiles' relationship to the body and to movement to be constant and important themes in Blaisse's work.

The collaborative Kassel project reflects a consistent development in Blaisse's career and ideas. Trained in textile design at the Gerrit Rietveld Academie in Amsterdam, where she was also a professor from 1974-87, Blaisse has crossed the boundaries of art, industry, performance and fashion with her concept of 'flexible design'. Since 1982, she has been exploring the industrial potential for creating flexible clothing using rubber laminates, synthetic foams, non-wovens and other new fibre technologies. The resulting totemic, stylised geometry of the one-off clothing works echo Oskar Schlemmer's costumes for the Bauhaus's *Triadic Ballet*, but her virtuoso handling of new technology has created a one-woman laboratory of ideas for industry.

Maria Blaisse's famous *Flexicaps* – a concept of futuristic hat shapes created from a one-cut basic concave and convex rubber form (the inner tube of a truck tyre) – led to a hat collection for Issey Miyake and indicate the thoroughness and diversity of her research. Looking for the appropriate production method with Vredestein, the Dutch rubber tyre company who supplied the material, Blaisse tried vacuum-moulding with polystyrenes, PVCs and non-wovens, immersion with latex, poured polyurethane, and compression injection-moulded rubbers. It was the latter which proved the most suitable, in terms of rigidity, tensile strength, suppleness, elasticity and colour fastness.

These discoveries led her to think about making moulded, cut and sealed one-piece garments, suggesting a new way of creating clothes to wear, but the Kassel project gave her the welcome opportunity to re-focus on process rather than product. She explains: 'The finest part of the fibre must be unravelled, so that every part of its meaning is displayed; then one can start using materials.' In researching a methodology of material, which expresses *itself* rather than expressing form, Blaisse is tapping a new aesthetic, reflecting changing values, morality and responsibilities of designers regarding the environment and what is produced for consumption.

Blaisse views the open-ended shared experience with her Kassel students as a 'beautiful exchange', which made participants more conscious of their own thoughts, priorities and approach. 'What happens to materials happens to yourself', she says; nature's life-cycle of development and ageing is paralleled in humans and in materials. By understanding the natural laws of material, she believes we can better understand human consciousness and nature. This is the impetus for her current work,

which can offer exemplars of new forms and applications for industry and other areas to build on. 'We shall not cease from exploration', she quotes from T S Eliot, 'and the end of all our exploring will be to arrive where we started and know the place for the first time.'

This intimate understanding of material and the aim to express its nature through invented form is also intrinsic to the work of Kyoko Kumai. 'I make things which I want to see, things I have never seen before', she says. Since 1976, when she took the unprecedented step of weaving thin steel wire to make textile art, Kumai has evolved an extensive personal vocabulary of techniques and forms for monumental sculptures and screens which has put her at the forefront of textile art in Japan.

Like Maria Blaisse, Kyoko Kumai regards East-West communication as important and inspirational. When I visited her compact, loom-laden studio in Japan recently, she spoke of the impact on Japanese textile art in the sixties of Western free-form hangings and sculptures, especially those of Sheila Hicks from American and Magdalena Abakanowicz from Poland. They inspired experimentation amongst the Japanese who then began to explore their own identity.

'The Orient – Japan, Korea, China – has a

Maria Blaisse
'Silver Spheres', 1989
Closed cell EVA foam
Photograph by Anna Beeke

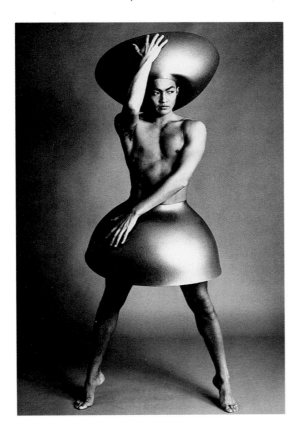

Ron Arad
'LoopLoop', 1993
Woven stainless steel welded
onto steel chair profiles
*Photograph by Christoph
Kicherer*

long history and it is important to express our own nature', says Kumai in acknowledging the now unmistakable characteristics of contemporary Japanese textile art. There is an emphasis on large-scale abstraction, often using a rhythmic repetition of elements; a close response to nature, to light, atmosphere and space; a dedication to harmony, reconciling order and chaos and the natural cycle of change, decay and renewal, and an intuitive sensitivity and constant adventurousness in the use of materials and techniques. This is emphasised by Kumai: 'It is very important to *make*. Western art theory is very strong, but Orientals make by feeling.'

Kyoko Kumai grew up by the sea and she views her work as 'a means of expression to explore various aspects of wind, air and light.' Her forms are at once animated yet contemplative, ethereal yet physically strong, filling interior space with compelling forms which suggest both the power of nature and of technology. Alchemy is at work, transforming prosaic industrial wire into elemental works of art. It is not surprising that Kumai has undertaken many public and corporate commissions and that the Department of Architecture and Design at the Museum of Modern Art in New York gave Kumai a solo show in 1991.

In choosing to work with various gauges of factory-made steel wire, and occasionally aluminium, over twenty years, Kumai has encountered and overcome 'many, many problems'. 'The material taught me the techniques', she says of the continuous inventiveness of her loom-woven and off-loom structures. She exploits the contrasting qualities of the material – stiff/soft, crinkly/sheer, sombre/glittering – through her techniques and through the incorporation of air and light to create subtle movement and iridescent surfaces and shadows. 'I am happy', Kumai concludes, 'if my works create a rich environment which surrounds the viewer, arousing various mental images and liberating the spirit.'

This search for new expressive forms is the impetus for the furniture and architecture of Ron Arad. It is interesting to see how the subversive irony of Arad's 1980s works – the recycled Rover car-seat chair, the traumatised metal-bashed tables and outsize armchairs – has yielded to poetic refinement. There is a narrative lyricism attached to Arad's wit in his designs which sets him apart from Philippe Starck and embeds his work more thought-provokingly in the memory. There is also a forceful link with pure sculpture which imbues it with another layer of meaning and purpose. Duchamp and Tinguely would approve.

Arad's experimental installation, *Sticks and Stones*, at the Centre Pompidou in 1987 and his recent installation piece of thirty tables at the Fondation Cartier in Paris are part of a continuous dialogue in all his work about form and function and the conventions of objects. Can't bookshelves be curvy (*Bookworm*, 1993) or an upholstered chair mean a standard wooden chair enclosed by a separate carapace of organic shining metal (*Chair by its Cover*, 1993)?

Ron Arad, Israel-born, London-based, architecture-trained, now works for several European design companies, including Kartell, Vitra, Driade and Moroso, and has moved the manufacture of his one-off and limited editions to Marzorati Ronchetti in Italy. His studio at Ron Arad Associates Ltd, his company in north London, no longer resounds to metal being welded and beaten, and this release from the demands of in-house production has enabled him to develop ambitious commissions such as the new Opera House interior in Tel Aviv.

Although Arad has expressed the view that no new chair design has been necessary since those of Thonet 100 years ago, it is precisely the fact that Arad's designs provide an antidote to modernist standardisation which helps to account for their appeal. The five chairs and daybeds group first made in 1992 allow rigid woven steel to mimic the fluid movement of cloth. Arad chose to work with stainless steel industrial conveyor-belt material, double-woven with a herringbone pattern, and had it polished, flatenned and cut to width. Literally, idea and material mesh; in one design (*London Papardelle*) the chair's extended floor 'rug' of metal can also be rolled up to create a footrest.

A similar conveyor-belt material appears in elements of his new Opera House interior for Tel Aviv and as the lining in a recent daybed design, but for the time being, as wood, bronze and plastics take over, it has passed into the repertoire. As Arad says, 'Ideas move on'.

The serendipity of opportunity and inspiration similarly affects the work of Tom Dixon. The opening of Space, his new retail outlet in west London, in addition to an interior design project in Africa, continued design work for Driade and his one-off furniture and lights, keep Dixon in the media and in the vanguard of new British design. Nevertheless, Dixon views his career as a struggle against the pervasive British 'lack of interest in modernity. People may wear Lycra clothes, but they're sitting on Laura Ashley furniture'.

This lack of interest among consumers means a damaging lack of investment in new interior design by British manufacturers and investors. One might hope to find new upholstery fabric designs on furniture in Britain, given the nation's devotion to comfy armchairs, but Dixon finds general taste in this area mired in a 1940s timewarp.

His insouciant 1980s furniture, such as the neo-Baroque, wrought-iron chairs using Victorian coal-hole covers as seats, attracted the label 'Postholocaust Chic' but by 1990 Dixon had perfected a classic 'S'-bend rush-woven chair which Driade snapped up for production. This textile element encouraged him to think of designing an upholstered piece when he saw the computer-designed tubular knitted jersey fabric by Karina Holmes, then a student at the Royal College of Art. For her degree show in 1992, Dixon designed a chaise longue with a steel frame and webbing to fit Holmes's graphic fabric.

Both Holmes and Dixon would be delighted to see this chaise longue in production backed by British investment, and many more ideas could follow: Holmes's portfolio spills over with samples of her computer-designed and knitted fabrics with graphics, textural surfaces (based on her photographs of fingerprints, skin, animal markings) and unconventional colour combinations. Although Courtaulds are now helping her to develop yarns, Holmes still works mainly in Italy for the car company Ghia on materials research and surface design.

The drain of British creative talent to the rest of Europe and to Japan and America is well-known, and the frustration amongst British designers is evident. Clearly, patterns of production are out of kilter with consumption in this country. In the furniture, glass, textile and ceramic industries here, the goal seems to be long runs of the same design, while the consumer wants variety and choice of colour, size, pattern, finish, and price.

Like Tom Dixon and Karina Holmes, the textile desginer Andrea Burkhard is committed to creating contemporary designs for interiors.

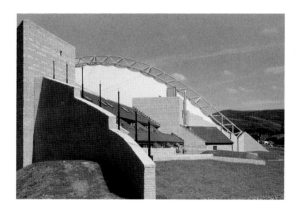

D Y Davies Associates
Royal International Pavilion,
Llangollen
© D Y Davies Associates

In Switzerland, however, her career suggests a more fruitful relationship between art and industry. Rohner Textile AG, the Swiss manufacturing company which staunchly backs Burkhard's ideas, researches and prototypes, were gratified to see her win the Swiss product design prize in 1993, for her series of rubber and raffia modular floor mats for sitting.

Andrea Burkhard's initial training as a draughtswoman for structural engineering and subsequently as a Jacquard weaver are evident in the harmonizing geometry of shape and texture in her designs, from the one-off shawls and floor mats to industrially-manufactured bed linen. Her works offer a visual counterpoint to those of Maria Blaisse and Kyoko Kumai, but all acknowledge the importance of nature and elicit a reflective response.

Burkhard's spatial fastidiousness echoes Carl Andre, although the repeated but different elements in her work, like nature's stones and branches, together with the relief surfaces of her designs encourage the play of changing light, colour and shadow to extend the visual impact of her work. As with all those working 'across the divide', the development of form lies in a thorough investigation of materials. 'Raffia, nylon, rubber and copper, for example, have very different properties and can only be used in certain ways.' says Burkhard. 'The better I can understand and use a material, the better the product.'

The subtle articulation of interior space achieved by Andrea Burkhard would be a perfect foil to the dynamic fabric architecture created and engineered by partnerships such as D Y Davies Associates with Atelier One and the virtuoso combination of Michael Hopkins with Ove Arup. It was at the Montreal Expo in 1967 that ancient tented structures first received a contemporary interpretation using synthetic fabric. However, the German Pavilion there has subsequently been superseded by many structures around the world using flexible, low-maintenance, relatively inexpensive fabrics. Building uses include sports, leisure, warehousing and transport.

The Royal International Pavilion, Llangollen, designed by D Y Davies Associates in 1992 to accommodate the Eisteddfod festival in North Wales, is the largest insulated tensile structure in Britain. The roof, three layers of PVA-coated polyester, spans a 60-metre bowstring arch of tubular steel and rise to 23 metres at its highest point. The form complements the surrounding undulation of hills and the flexibility of structure can provide changes in seating capacity at different times of year.

The exciting potential for architecture offered by developments in synthetic fabrics is epitomised by the building for Schlumberger Research Ltd in Cambridge, completed in 1985. The architect was Michael Hopkins and structural engineers were Ove Arup (the membrane roof) and Anthony Hunt Associates (steel structures).

With this building, the use of a Teflon-coated glass fibre fabric for the gigantic membrane roof advanced both the state of architecture and engineering science. The building, which houses a testing station, laboratories, offices and seminar rooms for oil-industry related research, exudes the visual coherence of architectural minimalism. This is achieved by the reductionist refinement of components and detailing and by the choice of fabric roofing. Teflon-coated glass fibre is more translucent than PVC-coated materials and more permanent, with a life expectancy of twenty years. The fabric maintains its brightness, is highly resistant to fire, and dust attracted by static electricity is washed away by rain.

The Teflon coating is applied in layers to the glass fibre, which is woven like cloth, with forces concentrated along the weft to achieve the correct tensile strength when installed. To achieve the size, the membrane roof is made up of large flat strips of the fibres, which are lapped and heat-welded together. The specification of the fibre, its shape, pre-stressing method and testing for responses to wind loads and maintenance are all the responsibility of the engineer. The required surface stresses when installed are achieved by wrapping the perimeter of the fabric on 20-metre steel cables, and suspending the membrane on spiral steel cables from the main structural steel masts.

The spectacular technical and visual feat embodied by the innovate Schlumberger Research building was summarised by *The Architects' Journal* in October 1984: 'Ranking with the revolutionary structural developments that gave us the perpendicular style of English cathedral building, or the huge clear spans of the great Victorian railway sheds, the use of lightweight membranes provides an extraordinary opportunity for enclosing space and admitting natural light.'

The boundaries of technology, and of art, design and industry too, have indeed been extended by the research and development of new materials and techniques. As the work discussed here indicates, an inspired cross-fertilisation of ideas, reconciling the forces of nature with the impulses of human invention, continues apace.

Schlumberger Research Centre, Cambridge
Architect: Michael Hopkins
Engineers (roof): Ove Arup & Partners
© *Ove Arup & Partners*

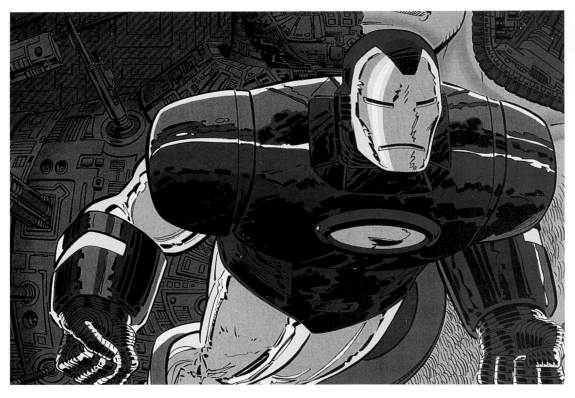

The alchemist's art

Marie O'Mahony

Alchemy was the ancient precursor to chemistry, and yet alchemy differed from the science of chemistry in both approach and objectives.[1] Alchemy existed as an art and philosophy well before rational thought laid the foundations of pure science. Alchemy also had a clear and singular goal, namely the creation of precious material (gold) from base elements. The processes by which futuristic textiles have been conceived and created, and the way in which their repercussions began to be felt, indicate that textile design, in its eclectic pursuit of new materials of value, is now at the alchemical stage in its evolution, as chemistry was centuries ago. Only this time, the alchemist's art is actually producing tangible results.

In an alchemical sense, textile designers are already having some success in creating valuable 'green' materials from the worthless refuse of contemporary society: plastics, old rags and discarded paper. In other areas, composites of resins and man-made fibres are combined to create materials with designer structural properties that were never achievable with the basic ingredients. Alloys are created with inherent 'memory' to enable them to return to preset shapes after massive distortion; these are then woven into fabric-based products that can exploit such properties. Clothing with incredible

fire-resistant properties realises the dreams of the Marvel Comic artists with their super-human creations. 'Intelligent' or 'smart' textiles are being used in architectural environments to replace static relationships with dynamic and changeable ones.

This essay looks into the green, super-human and smart areas. In assessing the potential impact of new textiles, the fabrics cannot simply be considered in the context of their physical value, but also in the context of the processes (this is as far as the alchemists ever got) involved in creation and the creators themselves. Finally, we observe the potential for analysing the alchemist's art itself as our design tools extend into new micro levels and sub-structures.

While textiles have been recycled industrially for over 150 years, it is only in the last ten years that the textile industry has shown serious interest in the process. Increased consumer awareness as well as more stringent international and government legislation on industrial waste have forced industry's hand.[2] Technology, particularly chemical, is one of the main sources of industrial pollution in the world today. It seems appropriate that technology should help provide solutions to some of the problems its misuse has caused in the past.

Mantero Seta, one of Italy's main silk

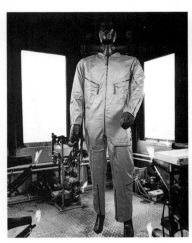

Du Pont
Thermo Man – today's superheroes are passive rather than aggressive protectors. Thermo Man is Du Pont's burn-test mannequin, used to evaluate the performance of protective garments under simulated flash fire conditions. The mannequin is dressed in the garment to be tested and exposed to a flash fire created to engulf it in flames for up to ten seconds. The 122 sensors record temperature rise on the surface of the mannequin. A sophisticated computer programme calculates, predicts and displays graphically the resulting area body burns, grading them as to their severity.
© *Photogaphs courtesy of Du Pont*

producers, set up a research centre headed by Luisa Cevese to look into ways of recycling the vast quantities of selvage (the edge of the cloth) waste produced in their silk factories. Working with a plastics company, Cevese produced some exciting experiments using heat and laminated forms of bonding combined with woven and felted fabrics. Although designers and fashion houses were interested, they demanded that the last metre of fabric be exactly the same as the first – impossible! The very nature and unique characteristic of recycled fabric has variety as its essence. The centre has since closed, but Luisa Cevese has continued the work as an independent designer. It would seem that, although industry is willing, the recycling process remains the tool of a few designers dedicated to promoting its philosophy.

Process dominates the work of Italian designer and architect Gaetano Pesce, and his choice of materials is never simply functional but based on his belief that his chosen materials, fabric-offcuts and urethane (one ecologically sound, the other toxic), act as a document of the time. He centres each project around the body as symbol of the nature within man helping to establish man's relationship with the world around him. In describing the *Children's Table & Chair*, Pesce comments that 'Children are naturally "softer"

than adults in both mind and body because they are still growing in every way. Since they are also very active, the things around them should be pliable'. Through the use of flexible materials, the designs become 'open', which allows them to be used both as furniture and as toys, depending on the participant's decision. Hence, for Pesce, recycling is incidental to his work, in contrast to Cevese's designs, which take re-use as their theme.

The advent of new technology has allowed many properties already present in textiles to be enhanced. This enhancement can be achieved by combining elements (fibres, chemicals, ceramics, metals) which have limited use individually but when combined, become very useful indeed.

Recent materials technology has increased the ability of textiles to give protection against the environment and hazardous conditions.[3] For instance, most clothing affords some protection against the sun's harmful rays simply because it forms a physical barrier between the skin and the sun. A Japanese company, Kuraray, have developed an ultraviolet (UV) ray blocking fibre, Esmo, which gives added protection. The fibre contains powdered ceramics which absorb some of the UV rays, while reflecting the heat rays. Increasingly, fabrics are being developed with specific functions, ranging from light-sensitive and anti-static to anti-bacterial and thermo-chromic (i.e. changing colour according to temperature).

While Marvel Comic's superhero Iron Man had his flexible suit of iron alloy, with its undreamed of powers of strength and flight, Du Pont's 'Thermo Man' sports a suit of Nomex Delta T which protects him against temperatures of over 350°C. This latest development is worn by many fire-fighters and combines the fire-protective qualities of Nomex with the durability under stress of Kevlar. As the line between science fiction fantasy and reality narrows through technological achievement, it is noticeable that the range widens considerably as to how this technology is used. Since the end of the Cold War, western defence industries are fast becoming one of the main developers of protective clothing. Initially this is intended for military use, but ultimately many of the materials developed could have civilian applications. Tents which protect their inhabitants against chemical and biological warfare are mentioned, but not discussed, by the British Defence Department. They are more open about variable pile fabrics which allow adjustable insulation against cold or heat. This increased development of protective clothing is the result of a demand from a society concerned with human welfare, a humanitarian society.

In order to expand the capabilities of the machine some responses have been built into them which allow them some 'initiative' in that they can react to situations and stimuli. This technology has started to leave the factories and find a useful place in our daily lives; in clothes which change colour according to the temperature, and in buildings which regulate the amount of sunlight allowed in. The name given to this technology is 'intelligent' or 'smart'.

Computer-based artificial intelligence (AI) was pioneered in the first half of this century by Alan Turing.[4] His legacy, the Turing Test, seeks to find a form of AI which can convince a panel of judges that it is human. So far no computer has succeeded. Smart materials is a good media buzz-word but the materials themselves, while having value, do not yet approach Turing's idea of AI. The 'smart' technology it refers to is responsive only in being able to react in a predetermined way to a stimulus or series of stimuli. Smart materials are only just starting to find useful applications, and perhaps the only limit to their possibilities is our imagination.

One of the earliest modern smart materials is Gore-Tex, invented twenty years ago, a 'breathing' membrane which allows body

Luisa Cevese
'Big Bag', 1992
Cotton and silk from industrial waste, E.V.A.
H 50 cm W 40 cm D 12 cm
Advancing the recycling process remains the task of a few dedicated designers.

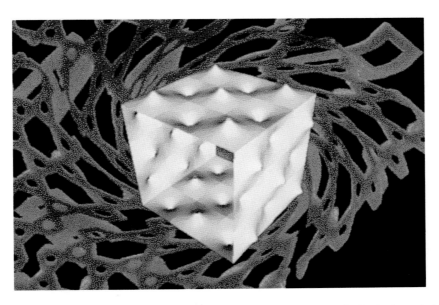

Ade Adekola
'Smart' fabric for architecture,
CAD image
Striving for the ultimate in
flexible buildings.
© Ade Adekola

moisture out without letting rain in. Today, we have materials which can decide what to allow in and out, unlike Gore-Tex which is indiscriminate or 'dumb'.

Responsive textile products vary from the visually active, such as a climbing rope which changes colour under stress,[5] to the visually passive such as the 'smart bra',[6] which regains its shape at certain temperatures during washing. These products are made from the same materials as their conventional counterparts with the addition of smart materials – for the rope a dye, and for the bra shape memory alloys (SMAs). There is potentially no limit to the number of responses a material can incorporate. A more complex system of responses is being developed in a carpet underlay which can monitor the characteristics of a person walking on the carpet – size of footprint, height, weight, sex. This could eventually have useful applications in the security industry. However, these are individual products. If smart materials are to realise their potential value they must be incorporated into our whole lifestyle.

Architecture is perhaps the most wide reaching of all the design disciplines in terms of its effect on people. Like all design, it relies on an interaction with people for its existence. Architects' interest in smart materials has come

from a desire to form better links between the building, the environment and its human occupants. Architect Lebbeus Woods looks for an architecture which will allow a more equable society where man and his environment can interact.[7] One step in this direction is being made at a Japanese university. where a tracking system is being developed which would be contained in carpet underlay and could be used by blind people to find their way around buildings. The system is designed to work via an earpiece connected to the blind person's cane which picks up messages from a recorded tape.

In Britain, architect Ade Adekola is working on a tensile roofing system which can respond to different stimuli: light, proximity and sound, depending on the sensors used. He looks forward to a time when one can arrive home from a busy day, sit on the sofa and have the room fabric respond to your mood! Using medical technology, his roofing system can measure the occupant's pulse rate and decide whether it should adopt soothing/lively/aggressive (physical) mannerisms.[8] Textiles have become particularly important to these developments because they can expand, contract and change shape easily, unlike traditional cladding materials of concrete and steel.

Smart materials are not purely the product of

human technological endeavours. In nature many species consist of mainly soft and wet substances, and some exist without a rigid frame of support. The sea cucumber is basically a water-swollen gel equipped with what we would regard as very primitive organs.[9] With these it feeds, reproduces and defends itself from predators. It protects itself by stiffening its usually flexible body when it is touched, before turning part of its body wall into a viscous fluid mass which prevents it being firmly grasped. Without the flexible body the whole process would not be possible and the creature would most likely be eaten by its larger predators. A flexible cladding is equally important to the functioning of many smart materials, the most versatile cladding is material of a tensile nature, including fabrics, composites and fibres. This is not to say that textiles form the core element in the development of this technology but they do aid its realisation.

Researchers are examining the process by which technology functions in order to see its effect on textile design. Jonathan Fuller makes a design feature of the 'picts' or small square pixels which make up each image on the computer screen. Barbara Dass goes further, to the very core of the computer design process – its DNA. The computer is capable of generating very sophisticated textile designs and patterns, and it is possible to get to the very heart of its design process. By analysing how the computer goes about building a pattern one can intercept the process to emphasise patterns of 'growth', and allow the design to evolve. This has the potential to form a future textile design process which is evolving rather than static.

Today's alchemists are concerned with the environment in which we live and our relationship to it. Popular culture is by its nature a thermometer of society's fears and worries. For example, a new Sega computer game called Bio-Hazard depicts a world threatened by biological vermin and a collapsed ecosystem. In order to defeat the evil vermin, the player of Bio-Hazard has to adapt his skin and protective clothing equally aggressively. Let us hope that the new textiles won't be used to right the previous wrongs in this way!

The Rumpelstilskin who helped the miller's daughter spin straw into gold has been replaced by a whole network of alchemists from very different disciplines, all working together to create fabrics more precious even than gold.

Bio-Hazard
Nightmare vision of a system destroying itself.
© *Photograph courtesy of Sega UK*

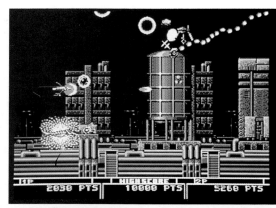

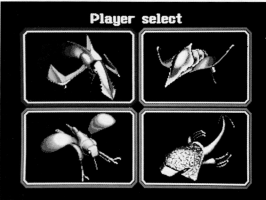

1. A useful exploration into the meanings of alchemy is offered by C J Jung in *Psychology and Alchemy*, Routledge, London 1989.
2. Cooper, Dr P, 'The Consequences of New Environmental Legislation on the UK Textile Industry', *Knitting International* 10/92, pp28-36.
3. 'The development of new fibres with sophisticated functions as high value-added products', *Knitting International* 6/92, p42.
4. Hodges, A, *Alan Turing – The Enigma of Intelligence*, Unwin Paperbacks, London 1987.
5. Cairngorm Climbing Rope Co Ltd.
6. Furukawa Electric Co Ltd.
7. *Lebbeus Woods* (Architectural Monograph 22), Academy Editions, London 1992
8. Adekola, Ade 'Touchy, Feely Structure', *New Scientist*, 31 October 1992, p19.
9. Osada, Yoshihido and Ross-Murphy, 'Intelligent Gels', *Scientific American* 5/93, pp42-47.

Biographies

Ade Adekola

Ade Adekola was born in Nigeria in 1966. He trained as an architect at the University of Manchester before attending the Architectural Association in London, qualifying with an AADipl in 1992. He has been involved with responsive and 'smart' materials for a number of years. Projects include *Self Inducing Device* (SID), a vertebrae-like structure which moves to attract the viewer, adopting different modes of behaviour (arrogant, bored, aggressive etc.) if the viewer fails to approach it. Other projects include a Passive Cooling Cladding System and a Dynamic Interactive Sheltering System. Adekola incorporates disciplines other than architecture in his projects, such as medical technology for measuring people's physiological states. He is currently involved in developing an intelligent tensile roofing system which will respond to external stimuli by changing shape. Depending on the sensors used it can respond to changes in light or sound as well as proximity. Since January 1993 Ade Adekola has been running Innovative Design Systems in London. His activities have expanded to include various product designs including the Aero-foil Lamp and Mono Pod Table. He has written various articles and reports on intelligent building systems for publications such as *New Scientist* and as co-author with W McLean, a report to the Earth Centre Project in 1993 on sustainable technologies. He is an avid collaborator.

'Smart' fabric for architecture, CAD image
© Ade Adekola

Ove Arup & Partners
Michael Hopkins & Partners

Ove Arup & Partners was founded by Ove Arup in 1946. They have worked alongside architects on some of the most important contemporary buildings including the Sidney Opera House, the Pompidou Centre and the Lloyds' of London building. They have been involved in tented structures since the late sixties and stressed roofing fabric since the early seventies. Ove Arup's original philosophy of working to a common end rather than seeking individual prominence is still strong in the practice and is particularly important in collaborative ventures with architects. The Schlumberger Research Centre in Cambridge was one such collaboration with Michael Hopkins & Partners.

Michael Hopkins & Partners was formed in 1976 and works from a London office which the practice designed and built in 1984. Two of their best-known tensile-related structures – Schlumberger Research Centre in Cambridge and the Mound Stand, Lord's Cricket Ground – are the subjects of books published by Phaidon. Current projects include the rebuilding of Glyndebourne Opera House. Michael Hopkins is a member of the Arts Council Architecture Advisory Panel, RIBA and the Architectural Association Councils. Michael and Patty Hopkins recieved the 1994 Royal Gold Medal for Architecture.

MOMI hospitality tent
© *Ove Arup and Partners*

Ron Arad was born in Tel Aviv in 1951 and studied at the Jerusalem Academy of Art and at the Architectural Association in London. In 1981 he founded the design company One Off with Caroline Thorman. Arad's constant experimentation with steel and his radical reconception of the form and structure of furniture has put him at the forefront of contemporary design. Arad's 1992 collection took his research in metal fabrication a step further with the introduction of woven steel. For the first time steel not only appeared soft but actually behaved like fabric. An example, the *Looploop*, is an endless strip of herringbone doubleweave steel welded to two steel profiles without any additional structure.

Arad has designed collections for various international manufacturers including Moroso, Vitra, Kartell and Driade. Exhibitions include *Sticks and Stones*, Vitra Museum, Weil am Rhein, 1990; *Ron Arad*, Centre for Contemporary Art, Warsaw; Metropolitan Museum of Art, New York, 1993; and *Nouvelles Tendances*, Centre Pompidou, Paris, 1987.

In 1989 Arad founded Ron Arad Associates with Caroline Thorman and Canadian architect Alison Brooks. Arad and Brooks are currently working on several architectural projects including the public spaces of the new Israeli Opera House in Tel Aviv, a house/publishing studio in Germany, and restaurants in London. The Ron Arad Studio was established in Italy in 1994 to take over the production of the London workshop. Ron Arad is a professor of Industrial Design at the Hochschule für Angewandte Kunst in Vienna.

'Doubletake', 'No Duckling No Swan', and 'Soft in the Head', 1992
Woven polished stainless steel welded onto mirror-polished stainless steel walls
Photograph by Christoph Kicherer

Bobbi Shortlidge

Bobbi Shortlidge was born in 1944 in the United States and gained her BFA in commercial art at the University of Kansas. She went on to study part-time at the School of the Art Institute, Chicago where she developed an interest in weaving and learned how to use computers. She was technical weaving consultant at the School of the Art Institute, where she taught the computerised loom and CAD for several years. She is currently working towards a Master of Fine Arts, specialising in fibre, at Rhode Island School of Design, Providence. Shortlidge creates fabrics for industry and unique works for exhibition as well as working to commission. She is very interested in graphic, geometric shapes inspired by architecture and machinery. From this initial starting point she both designs and weaves using the computer, the results often being complex, double-weave structures which create a *trompe l'oeil* effect. Her work has been exhibited in the United States and Japan.

'Woven Bands No. 7', 1993
Woven cotton
H 81.5 cm W 89 cm
This panel is made of wool and is a plain weave, double cloth constructed on a computer loom.
© *Courtesy of the Art Institute of Chicago*
Photograph by Cathy Carver

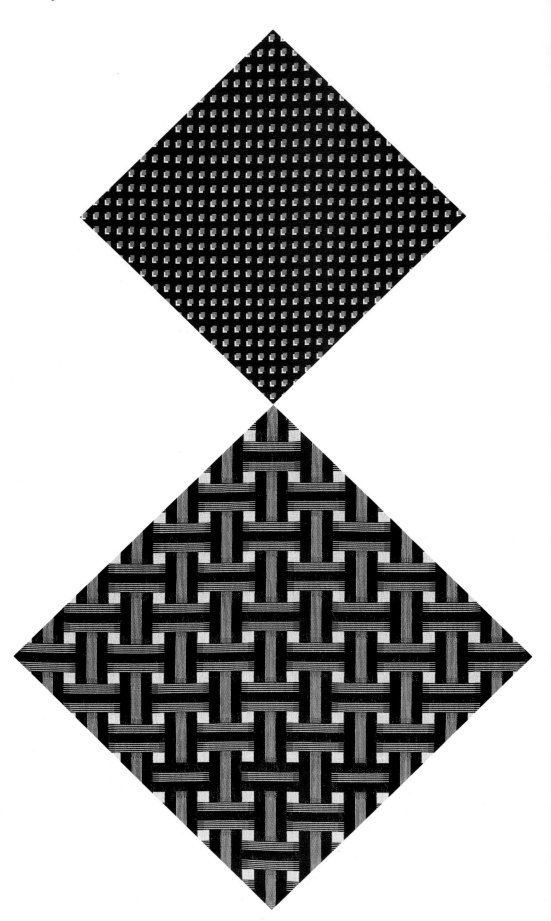

Pēteris Sidars

Pēteris Sidars lives and works in Latvia. He was born in 1948 and studied ceramics at the Liepaja School of Applied Arts before going on to study textiles at the Latvian Academy of Arts in Riga. He gets his inspiration from waste and mass-produced materials with tactile qualities, buying the materials in bulk before turning them into artworks. Recent work has incorporated fibre optic filaments which are woven with synthetic yarn before being rolled to form the finished sculpture. He has exhibited widely in Europe and the United States, taking part in many of the major textile biennales and triennales over the past ten years including the 1992 Lausanne Biennale and the fifth, sixth and seventh International Biennales of Miniature Textiles in Szombethely, Hungary.

Woven fibre optic
H 185 cm W 125 cm D 40 cm
The vivid, synthetic colours achievable with fibre optics produce a dramatic work in 'The Sun'.
Sponsor: Lattelekom (Tilts Communications)

Reiko Sudo

Textiles and new technology

Reiko Sudo was born in 1953 in Ibaragi Prefecture, Japan and trained as a weaver. She has worked as a freelance textile designer for many Japanese companies including Kanebo Ltd, one of Japan's foremost textile firms. After meeting Junichi Arai in 1982 they set up Nuno Corporation, where she both manages the business and creates new designs from her base in Tokyo. Reido Sudo has exhibited her textiles in exhibitions and competitions in Japan, the United States and Europe and, like Junichi Arai, is very interested in combining traditional textile materials and techniques with new technology and new ways of working. Some of her fabrics are influenced by other disciplines, such as the Japanese car industry, which inspired the use of a fine spattering of stainless steel over polyester taffeta.

Top:
'Crackle Quilt', 1992
Wool and rayon quilted and chemical etched
L 300 cm W 117 cm
Wool and rayon are quilted and then printed with a chemical which etches away the rayon fibre leaving behind a distressed and altered surface. 'Crackle Quilt' is designed by Junichi Arai and manufactured by Nuno Corporation.
© Nuno Corporation

Middle:
'Stainless Steel Emboss', 1992
Woven and splatter-plated polyester
L 300 cm W 120 cm
'Stainless Steel Emboss' is designed by Reiko Sudo and manufactured by Kanebo Corporation. This is a plain weave using polyester yarn very finely spattered with stainless steel using techniques borrowed from the Japanese automobile industry. This variation is embossed during the finishing process.
© Nuno Corporation

Bottom:
'Agitfab', 1992
Polyester, fused with newspaper and sealed with vinyl chloride
L 300 cm W 117 cm
In 'Agitfab' Reiko Sudo uses a base fabric of polyester with newspaper clippings sealed by laminating the textile with vinylchloride. Manuafactured by the Nuno Corporation.
© Nuno Corporation

Junichi Arai

Junichi Arai was born in 1932 in Kiryu City, Gunma Prefecture, Japan. Together with Reiko Sudo he established Nuno Corporation in 1983, a textile company specialising in woven fabric combining ancient, Japanese weaving techniques with the latest technologies. Junichi Arai is based in Kiryu (famous for its Jacquard weaving), where he works directly with the textile manufacturer. He learnt about the world of textiles from an early age as his grandfather was a spinner and his father a weaver and he continues in this tradition. He is a pioneer and has gained three dozen patents for developments incorporating new technology, exploiting the characteristics of natural and synthetic yarns and using computers as a tool to enable the most unpredictable and wonderful fabrics. He began using the computer in textile design in 1979 and has revolutionised the Jacquard weaving process. His fabric designs have been in exhibitions in Japan, the United States, Canada and England, and he has supplied fashion designers such as Issey Miyake and Rei Kawakubo. In 1987 he received the award of Royal Designer for Industry in England. Nuno is based in Toyko and has showrooms in New York and Los Angeles.

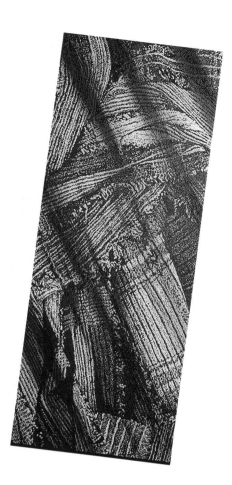

Left:
'Basket Weave Big Pockets', 1990
Cotton woven on a computer-assisted Jacquard loom
L 300 cm W 90 cm
This computer-assisted Jacquard double weave combines fine cotton threads with knitted tubes creating a rich and varied texture. The computer allows great changes in woven pattern (pockets are created in areas using the double weave structure) and yarn thickness, resulting in complex patterns and a textile which is different on both sides. Designed by Junichi Arai and manufactured by Nuno Corporation, Japan.
© Nuno Corporation

Centre:
Woven Structure Pattern, 1983
Cotton woven on a computer-assisted Jacquard loom
L 300 cm W 90 cm
A traditional African woven fabric was photocopied and translated into a computer programme. The resulting design was then woven on a computer-assisted Jacquard loom, the textural surface being achieved by using highly twisted cotton yarn. Designed by Junichi Arai and manufactured by Nuno Corporation, Japan.
© Nuno Corporation

Right:
'Big Checkerboard', 1985
Nylon woven on a dobby loom
L 300 cm W 115 cm
In 'Big Checkerboard' three different types of nylon are combined in a woven structure. In the finishing process they react against eachother - some shrinking and blistering to create an unpredictable effect. Designed by Junichi Arai and manufactured by Nuno Corporation.
© Nuno Corporation

Andrea Burkhard

Andrea Burkhard was born in 1956 in Switzerland and studied textiles at the Schule für Gestaltung, Zürich, after undertaking training in structural engineering. She works as an artist and as a freelance textile designer for companies such as Rohner Textil AG. She also lectures at the Schule für Gestaltung, Zürich. Inspired by nature, she explores a variety of materials such as raffia, rubber, copper and nylon, using weaving techniques to create both designs for interior use and unique works for exhibition. Her seating mats are the result of research into the qualities of rubber and raffia and create a spatial dimension with their relief surfaces. They are intended to create a feeling of calm and are minimal in their aesthetic. Andrea Burkhard's work has won many awards including the 1993 Swiss Design Prize.

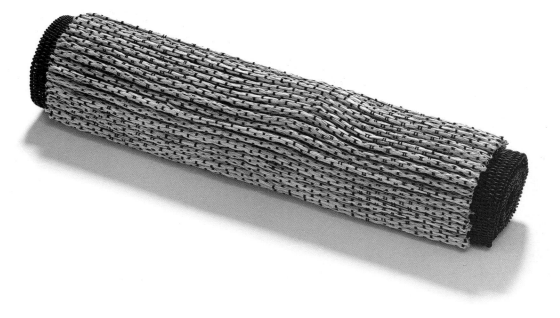

Top:
'Sitzmatte', 1991
Woven cotton and rubber
W 45 cm D 90 cm
Photograph by Roland Stucky
Bottom:
'Sitzmatte', 1991
Woven cotton, rubber and raffia
W 45 cm D 90 cm
Photograph by Roland Stucky

Atelier One/D Y Davies Associates

Atelier One was founded five years ago by Neil Thomas, Jane Witz and Reg Allen. All had previously worked for Anthony Hunt Associates. The company has worked on such projects as Ron Arad's studio and the Greenpeace Headquarters building (both in London), and the Eisteddfod Centre in Llangollen with D Y Davies Associates. In 1991 Atelier Ten was formed as an environmental engineering group headed by Steve Marshall and Patrick Bellew. The practices have joined forces on projects such as the Greenpeace Headquarters.

D Y Davies Associates was established in 1969 by its current chairman David Davies and is one of Britain's largest architecture practices. In 1986 the holding company, D Y Davies plc, became the first architectural practice to be quoted on the London Stock Exchange. The company has been involved in a wide ramge of projects, including Terminal 3, Heathrow, the Carlton Highland Hotel, Edinburgh, Harlow Business Park, to Sunningdale Golf Club. Current projects include an extension for the Guildhall Museum and Art Gallery in London, and Valle de Cerrato, Spain's first new town.

Royal International Pavilion, Llangollen
Photographs © D Y Davies Associates

Textiles and new technology

Maria Blaisse

Collaborative work between Maria
Blaisse and textile students at the
University of Kassel
These images illustrate the results of a
collaboration between Maria Blaisse and
textile students at the University of
Kassel in Germany. Thermoplastic, non-
woven fabrics were used and
transformed by heat to create costumes
which are richly variant in form.

Maria Blaisse was born in 1944
in Amsterdam. She studied textile
design at the Gerrit Rietveld
Academie, Amsterdam, then
worked in the design studio of
Jack Lenor Larsen, New York, and
researched textile techniques in
South America for two years. Maria
Blaisse was a professor in textile
and flexible design at the Gerrit
Rietveld Academie for fourteen
years while investigating textiles
and exhibiting the results as forms
which relate to the human body.
Since 1982 Maria Blaisse has
been researching industrial
applications for non-woven
materials, rubber laminates and
synthetic foams. The results are
dynamic and unconventional,
challenging the previous use of
these materials. She has worked
with Issey Miyake, designing hats,
and has created costumes for
dance and opera productions
around the world.

55

Emily DuBois

Emily DuBois was born in 1946 and lives in Kansas City. She studied textiles at Rochester Institute of Technology, New York, and at the California College of Art and Crafts. DuBois works as a textile artist, specialising in woven and dyed fabrics. She is especially interested in combining traditional textile techniques such as *shibori* with the technology of a computer-assisted loom. The resulting textile artworks are complex, fully utilising the intricate patterning and structures that this technology facilitates and yet possessing a visual unity. Her sources of inspiration are natural imagery, energy and growth patterns, reinforced by her strong interest in Taoist philosophy. She has exhibited her work throughout the USA.

'Fragment'
Woven on a computer-assisted loom
L 142.5 cm W1 17 cm
Photograph by Carley Fonville

Jonathan Fuller

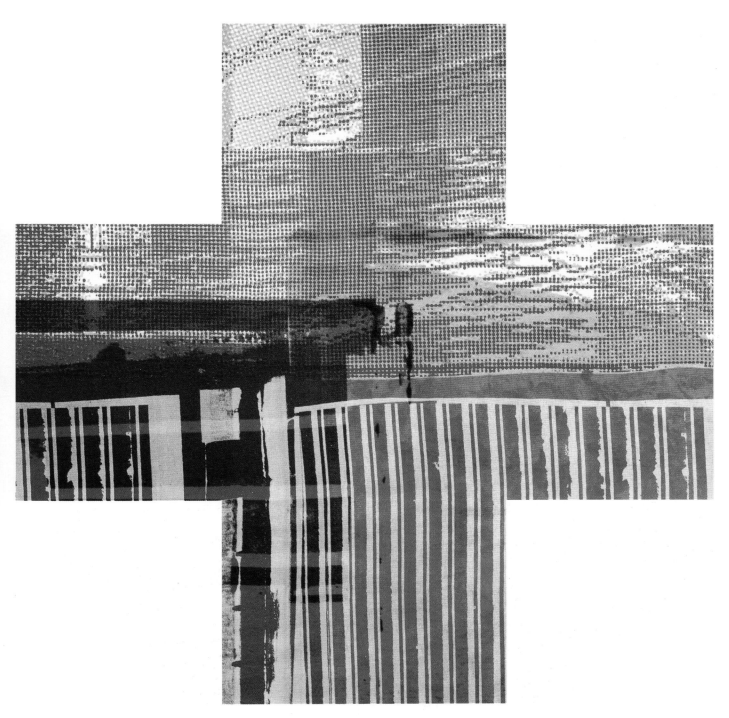

Jonathan Fuller was born in 1971 in Cornwall and now lives and works in London. He studied design at Glasgow School of Art, graduating in 1992. He designs using computer drawing and painting programmes, distorting and manipulating images which are then silk-screen printed by hand. He takes full advantage of the manual process to allow further manipulation and over-printing at the printing stage. He has exhibited in many of the major textile shows including the Fashion Foundation and MITI Japan in 1992 where he was a finalist in the International Textile Design Contest. Other awards include a British Airways Banner Competition and a Paperchase Design Award.

Luisa Cevese

Luisa Cevese was born in 1955 in Milan. She is a self-taught designer, working in the areas of textiles and art since 1978. Cevese was Director of Centro Richerche Mantero in Como from 1988 to 1993. This research centre was free from commercial limitations, and attracted interest worldwide.

She is now working as a freelance designer and artist and sells her work to fashion and interior designers, advertising companies, textile industries and interior and accessory stores. Clients include Dolce & Gabbana, Romeo Gigli, Chanel and Padova. At present she is particularly involved in the

Riedizioni Project – textiles and products made out of industrial waste. These works refer back to the human ability to make something useful from scraps (for example, patchwork), and take advantage of technology, enabling them to be competitively priced and yet retain a hand-made quality.

'Bag with Zip', 1992
Cotton and silk from industrial waste,
E.V.A.
H 43 cm W 27 cm D 8 cm

Harold Cohen

Harold Cohen is the Director of the Center for Research in Computing and the Arts at the University of California at San Diego. He was born in Britain and studied as a painter before becoming interested in artificial intelligence in the seventies. Since then he has worked almost exclusively with computers, occasionally collaborating with artists and crafts people in other media. He has collaborated with the Edinburgh Tapestry Company, commenting: 'I thought it was the most gorgeous object I had ever had any part in'. The Edinburgh Tapestry Company, founded in 1912 by the Fourth Marquess of Bute and often referred to as the Dovecot Studios, practices a traditional Gobelin technique and has collaborated with many of Britain's leading artists including Stanley Spencer, Henry Moore, Graham Sutherland and David Hockney.

Harold Cohen/Edinburgh Tapestry Company
'White Computer Tapestry', 1983
Cotton and wool, hand-woven
H 178 cm W 259 cm

Vibeke Riisberg

Vibeke Riisberg was born in 1951 in Copenhagen. She studied textiles at the Danish School of Art and Design in Copenhagen, specialising in printed textiles and at the Visual School of Arts, New York, in computer graphics. Between 1982 and 1992 she set up the textile design studio, Tastemain and Riisberg, which was based in Paris and since 1980 has been Professor at the Danish School of Art and Design. Vibeke Riisberg creates textile designs for interior use which are manufactured by the Danish textile company, Kvadrat, as well as unique lengths for exhibition. Since 1987 she has experimented with computer design and gained a scholarship from the Danish National Bank to enable her to develop this further. She combines the ancient technique of marking a surface with generating patterns on the computer screen to produce printed textiles. The results retain the spatial effect of the computer image and possess a wonderful dynamic vitality.

Above
Curtain 'Impression', 1992
Cotton satin designed on a Mac II by Vibeke Riisberg, manufactured by Kvadrat
L 320 cm W 140 cm D 10 cm
© Photographer Ole Akhoj/maker/Kavdrat

Below
Curtain 'Vibration', 1992
Cotton satin designed on a Mac II by Vibeke Riisberg, manufactured by Kvadrat
L 320 cm W 140 cm D 10 cm
© Photographer Ole Akhoj/maker/Kavdrat

Warren Seelig

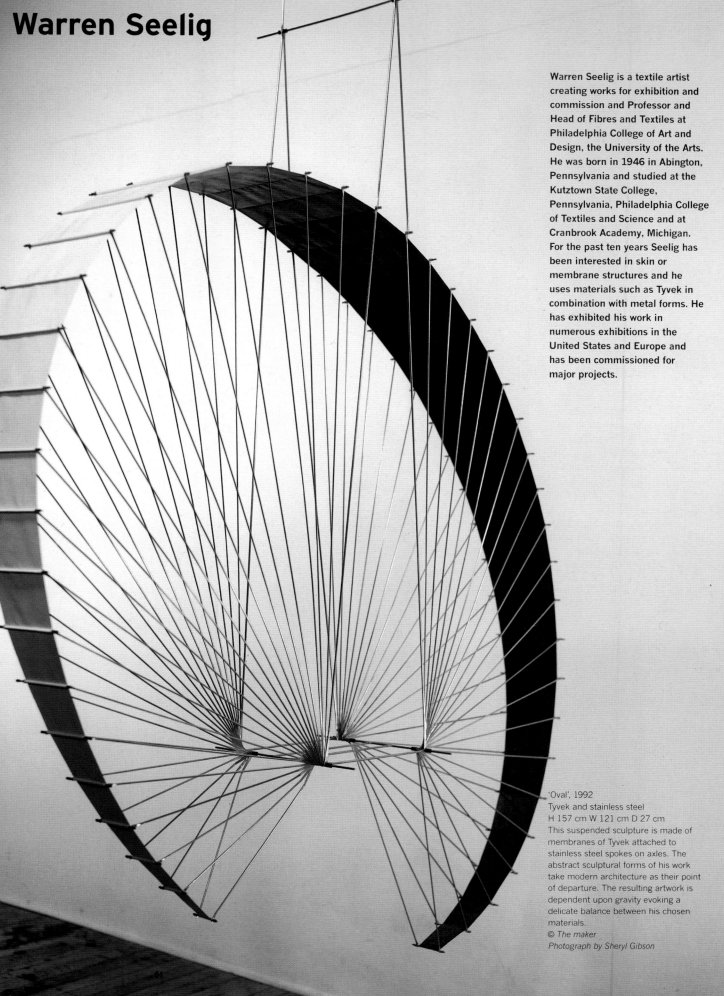

Warren Seelig is a textile artist creating works for exhibition and commission and Professor and Head of Fibres and Textiles at Philadelphia College of Art and Design, the University of the Arts. He was born in 1946 in Abington, Pennsylvania and studied at the Kutztown State College, Pennsylvania, Philadelphia College of Textiles and Science and at Cranbrook Academy, Michigan. For the past ten years Seelig has been interested in skin or membrane structures and he uses materials such as Tyvek in combination with metal forms. He has exhibited his work in numerous exhibitions in the United States and Europe and has been commissioned for major projects.

Biographies

'Oval', 1992
Tyvek and stainless steel
H 157 cm W 121 cm D 27 cm
This suspended sculpture is made of membranes of Tyvek attached to stainless steel spokes on axles. The abstract sculptural forms of his work take modern architecture as their point of departure. The resulting artwork is dependent upon gravity evoking a delicate balance between his chosen materials.
© The maker
Photograph by Sheryl Gibson

Cynthia Schira

Cynthia Schira is an American artist. She attended the Rhode Island School of Design in 1956 before studying at L'Ecole d'Art Décoratif in Aubusson, France and completing her MFA at the University of Kansas in 1967. Since then she has taught as Assistant, Associate and finally as Professor of Design at the University of Kansas from 1976–86. In 1991 she was one of a group of artists to be invited by the German company Müller-Zell to experiment with their latest CAD/CAM systems and electronic Jacquard looms. The technology of her artwork, *Repeated Hommage*, is described by Müller-Zell in the project's exhibition catalogue: 'This latest Jacquard technology makes artistic one-off items and small series affordable for individual use, thus helping democratise high standard textile art.' Schira has exhibited widely in the United States and Europe; she has held one-person shows at the Franklin Parrasch Gallery, New York and the Museum Bellerive in Zürich. Her work is included in several important public collections such as the Metropolitan Museum of Art and the Cooper-Hewitt Museum in New York.

'Repeated Hommage', 1991
Woven cotton
© *Photograph courtesy of Franklin Parrasch Gallery, New York*

Nigel Marshall

Nigel Marshall was born in 1958 in Britain. He studied at Winchester School of Art, specialising in constructed textile design for his first degree and in woven, knitted and printed plastics for his postgraduate research diploma. He lectures at various institutions in and around London and is currently working towards a PhD at the Royal College of Art, London. His thesis is entitled *The Design, Development and Production of Constructed Textiles Using Non-yarn Forms.* Marshall has been investigating composites and plastics for many years and combines traditional textile techniques such as weaving and knitting with new materials like slit film and plastics. These materials are subjected to various finishing treatments (laminating, heat-bonding, heat-transfer printing and vacuum-forming) which alter their configuration. The resulting work demonstrates a wide variety of decorative surfaces and structures for potential application. Marshall has exhibited his work in Britain and was an exhibitor and semi-finalist in Fatex 91, Tokyo, and the International Textile Fair (1989 and 1991) in Kyoto where he showed his laminated and heat-bonded textiles.

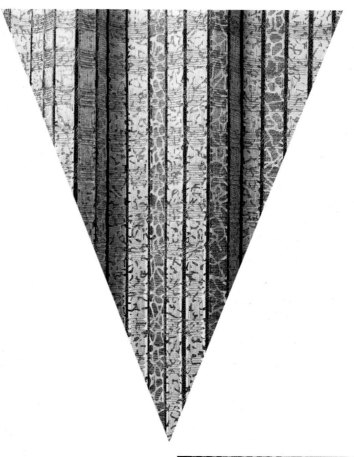

Above:
Untitled, 1993
Knitted plastic and metal
Below:
Untitled, 1993
Woven slit film with metallic thread and plastic
Opposite:
Woven slit film with metallic thread and plastic
Textiles by Nigel Marshall showing the results of much research into plastic materials. Here he uses slit nylon monofilament in a plain weave to create a structure which is laminated and then diagonally cut. This means that the surface is flexible in many directions as well as being very strong.
Photographs by Frank Thurston

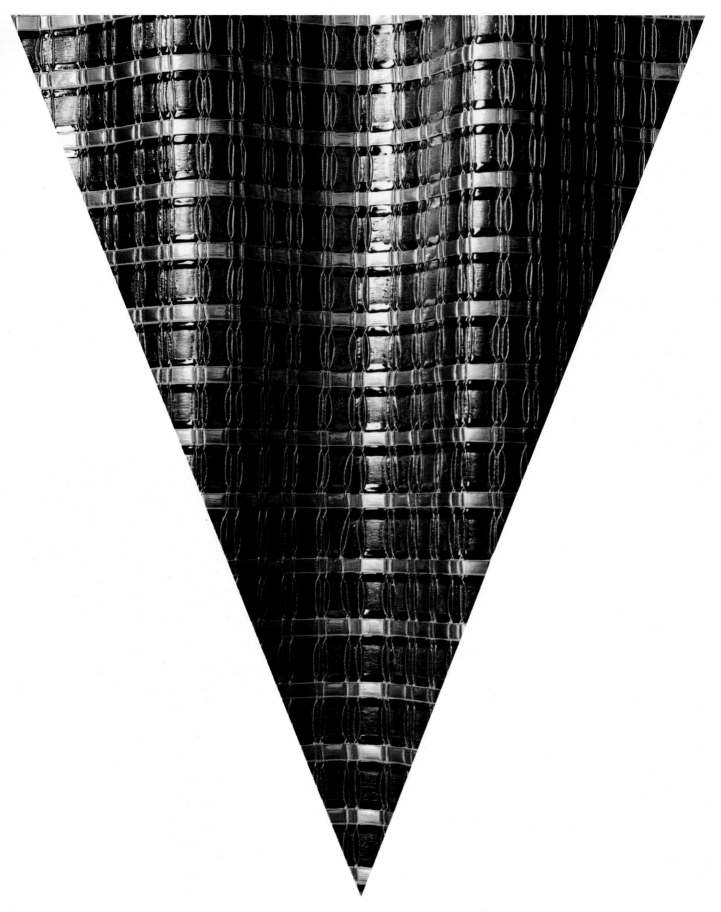

Kyoko Kumai

'Sen Man Na Yu Ta', 1994
Stainless steel filaments
H 200 cm W 300 cm D 30 cm

Kyoko Kumai was born in 1943 in Tokyo. She studied at Tokyo University of Arts in the Visual Design Department. She currently lives in Oita-City where she is both textile artist and Professor at Oita Prefectural Junior Art College. Over the past twenty years her work has evolved from the early pieces which used traditional textile materials and techniques. Since 1982 she has employed stainless-steel thread which she constructs to create textile artworks ranging from wall-based relief pieces to fully sculptural installations. A solo exhibition at the Museum of Modern Art, New York in 1991 established her as one of the leading contemporary Japanese textile artists. Kyoko Kumai uses industrial materials to express nature, her source of inspiration. Her work has been awarded many prizes including the New Technology Prize in the first International Textile Competition in Kyoto, 1987.

66

Gaetano Pesce

Child's table and chair
Recycled fabric and urethane
© Pesce Ltd

Gaetano Pesce was born in La Spezia, Italy in 1939. He graduated from the Faculty of Architecture at the University of Venice in 1965 and went on to study at the experimental Venice College of Industrial Design. Pesce is best known for his multi-disciplinary approach incorporating architecture, industrial design, sculpture, fashion and urban planning. He has been developing a relationship with industry for a number of years and worked with companies such as Cassina, B & B Italia, Knoll International and Vitra International. He has always taken an experimental and open approach to the possibilities offered by materials. The Pratt Chairs (1983) are a series of nine chairs made from urethane, which explore the utilitarian and symbolic function of an object by their varying degrees of softness and hardness. The Museum of Modern Art and the Metropolitan Museum, New York and the Centre Pompidou, Paris have his work in their collections. He was the subject of a recent monograph, *Gaetano Pesce* by France Vanlaethem (Thames & Hudson 1989). He lives and works in New York.

Anne Mieke Kooper

Anne Mieke Kooper was born in 1944 and lives and works in Amsterdam. She studied textile design at the Gerrit Rietveld Academie, Amsterdam, with a particular interest in rugs and carpets. After completing an apprenticeship with Jack Lenor Larsen in New York, she worked there for a year as a designer and now works freelance for them and other companies. Kooper currently lectures in textile design at the Gerrit Rietveld Academie. The majority of her design work involves computer-based technology; she designs and weaves on a computer-controlled loom. She is currently involved in research into flatwoven pile fabrics for rugs and upholstery.

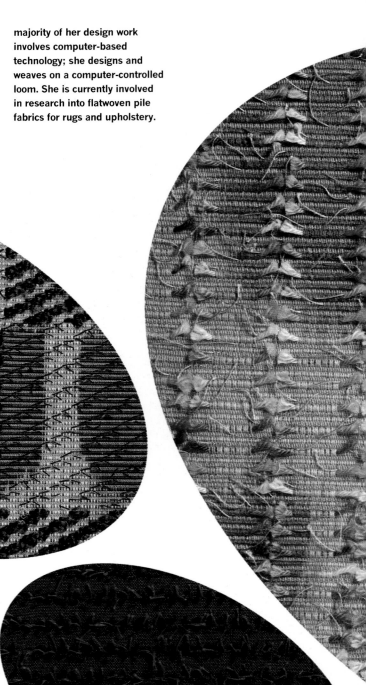

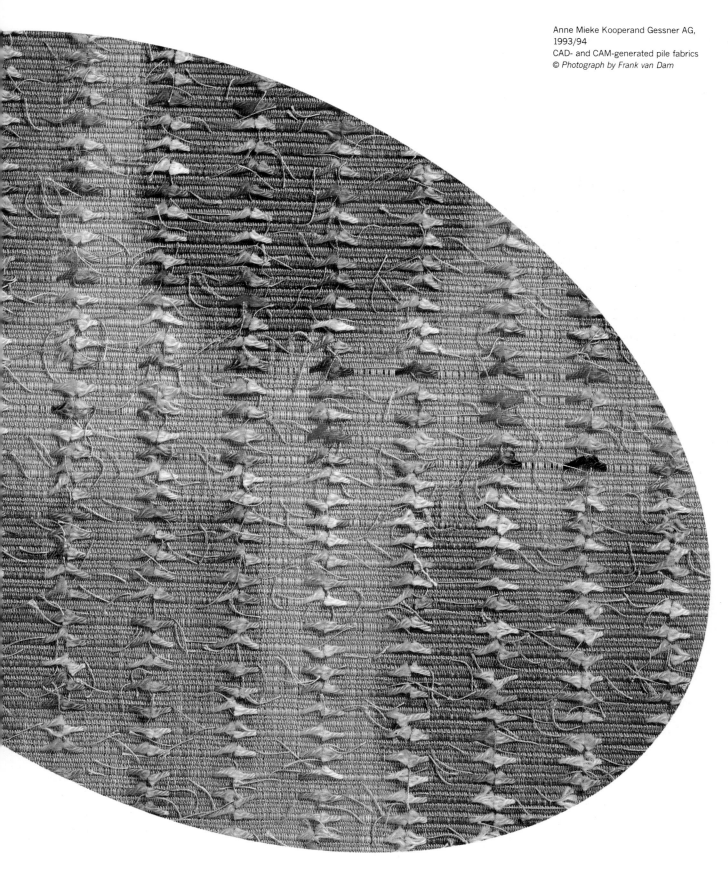

Anne Mieke Kooperand Gessner AG,
1993/94
CAD- and CAM-generated pile fabrics
© *Photograph by Frank van Dam*

Karina Holmes/Tom Dixon

Karina Holmes is a recent graduate of the Royal College of Art in London. Born in Britain, she now lives in Italy, working for the Ghia S.P.A. Design Centre. She received a Textile Institute Scholarship from 1985–89 while at the University of Leeds, and she won first prize in the Courtelle Fabric Awards in 1989. Karina Holmes has been involved with technology both in the design and manufacture of her knitted fabrics. Many are knitted on an 18-gauge Morat circular jersey machine and some include padding for use in upholstery fabrics, as in her collaboration with British furniture designer Tom Dixon.

Born in Sfax in Tunisia in 1959, Tom Dixon has lived in Britain since 1963. His work is collected internationally by museums such as the Musée des Arts Décoratifs,

Paris; the Pompidou Centre, Paris, the Vitra Museum, Weil am Rhein, the Brooklyn Museum, New York and the Boston Museum of Fine Art. English collections showing his work include the Victoria and Albert Museum, the Crafts Council and The Design Museum. Clients include Comme des Garçons, Jean Paul Gaultier, Romeo Gigli, Paul Smith, Gloria Thum und Taxis, Phillip Treacy and Vivienne Westwood. He has worked on numerous interior design commissions including several collaborations with Nigel Coates, and specially commissioned architectural lighting for interiors such as Pont de la Tour and The Alaska Works in London. His London shop, SPACE, is dedicated to presenting the work of young British and European designers.

'Rocking Chaise', 1994
Jersey fabric – wool, elastomeric fibre and polyester, CAD designed
H 110 cm L 150 cm W 50 cm
Photograph by Travis

Patrice Hugues

Patrice Hugues is a French artist and writer, born in 1930. He has developed a technique of heat-transfer printing which enables him to create high fidelity monoprints on sheer fabrics. The larger works are often suspended from the ceiling, allowing the fabrics to hang freely, creating a kinetic effect as the image shimmers in response to passing people. He has also produced artist's books, his most recent being *La Pêche au Linge*, 1986-88. This uses the same printing techniques as the larger artworks but emphasises the semi-transparency of the fabrics, allowing images from previous and succeeding pages to form part of the open pages. He has exhibited widely in Europe (Lausanne Biennale) and Japan; recent one-person shows include the Galerie Nationale de la Tapisserie, Beauvais, Paris; Musée de l'Impression sur Etoffes, Mulhouse, and Alain Oudin et Filotheque DMC, Paris. Hugues has written two important books on textiles: *Le Langage du Tissu*, 1982 and *Tissu et Travail de Civilisation*, 1993. He is represented by Alain Oudin – Paris.

Artist's book, 'La Pêche au Linge'
1986-88
© *Alain Oudin, Paris*

Crissij van den Munckhof

Above:
Le Corbusier's Notre-Dame du Haut, Ronchamp
© *Photograph by Tim Benton*
Left:
'Ronchamp', 1992
Felvet – polyurethane and nylon
W 51 cm D 31 cm
Crissij van den Munckhof is inspired by the wonderful curved roof of Le Corbusier's church at Ronchamp.
© *Photograph by Richard Dean*

Crissij van den Munckhof was born in 1962 in Hastings, New Zealand and now lives and works in London. She is self-taught; her work in contemporary art together with an interest in the industrial development and application of new materials led to the creation of alternative, wearable forms. The new fabric Felvet was developed over eight months in collaboration with various chemical specialists, resulting in a material which retains a strong memory while being soft and flexible. Felvet is used in her hat designs, which emphasise the textile by using simple yet dramatic shapes. She is currently investigating new textures, pile surfaces and moulding of forms.

Tent design: past and present

Brian Forster, Ove Arup & Partners, London

The art of tent making has been enjoying something of a renaissance in recent years. The last time this happened was in the nineteenth century when the circus began to establish itself as a major form of entertainment, firing the people's imaginations and becoming immensely popular. Initially performances took place in large halls in major towns and cities, but in 1860 a radical departure occurred in the United States. The railway network had by this stage opened up the country, and circus companies began travelling by rail to perform all over the United States in towns without such halls.

Large canvas structures were conceived which could be quickly assembled and dismantled at each stop, and so the large circus tent came into being. A visit to Paris in 1867 by the 'First American Railway Circus', complete with its tent and technical apparatus, aroused great public excitement and led to the formation of mobile groups in Europe. The tents, such as the classic chapiteau, were up to 50 metres in diameter and made from machine-woven linen or hemp canvas.

Centuries earlier it is thought that the Romans used retractable woven awnings, called *velaria*, to shade spectators in their amphitheatres. Frescoes in Pompeii dating from AD 79 show

a theatre largely covered with fabric slung between ropes suspended from the rim of the outer wall. Indeed, around the top storey of the Roman theatres at Pompeii, Paestum, Orange and the Coliseum in Rome there are attachment points for masts capable of supporting networks of such ropes. Comparable in a minor way, toldos have been used to shade Spanish streets since the sixteenth century, and similar awnings cover streets in Japan today.

Our contemporary parallels are the textile shade roofs over football and athletics stadiums built in the last six years in Bari, Rome, Stuttgart, Riyadh and Hong Kong. Even more fantastic are the totally enclosed arenas in the United States and Japan where anything from 40,000 to 70,000 spectators sit under naturally lit translucent roofs with clear spans of more than 200 metres.

So why this renaissance?

A major reason is the development of new

materials. In modern buildings, long-term durability and behaviour in fire are of paramount importance. In the early 1970s DuPont developed a polytetrafluoroethylene (PTFE) resin containing microscopic glass beads which could successfully be coated on to woven glass cloth whose yarns were spun from 3 micron diameter filaments produced by Owens Corning. The first membrane roof was made with this material in 1973 at La Verne College in California. PTFE, with its chemical stability, weathers well and the glass textile base ensures a material of very low combustibility. More structures quickly followed in the United States and large tensioned membrane roofs have been built over retail stores, airport terminals and sports facilities. In 1981 the world's largest membrane roof was built at Jeddah airport using PTFE/glass material. This is the Haj Terminal and provides 420,000 square metres of shade for pilgrims en route to Mecca.

In the very different climate of Japan substantial and impressive structures are also being built. An example is the Akita Sky Dome, a recreational building constructed in 1990. It is a very elegant single span steel ribbed vault incorporating its own warm air snow-melt system, and is covered by a highly translucent PTFE/glass membrane skin. The same material

Opposite:
Interior of Georgia Dome, Atlanta
Architect: Thompson Ventulett Stainback
Engineer: Weidlinger Associates
© *Photograph courtesy of Birdair*

Above right:
Chapiteau Tent
© *Photograph courtesy of IL Archiv*
Left:
Haj Pilgrim Terminal, Jeddah
Architect/engineer: Skidmore, Owings & Merrill
© *Photograph Owens Corning*

Left:
San Nicola Stadium, Bari, Italy
Architect: Renzo Piano
Engineer (roof) Ove Arup & Partners
© *Photo: Ove Arup & Partners*

was used for the roofs of both the Rome Stadium and the Bari Stadium, designed for the 1990 soccer World Cup.

It is not simply the advent of new materials that has caused renewed activity in the tent world. Engineering design has developed quite radically due to the intellectual understanding of the action and behaviour of these structures and computer power assists in converting three-dimensional shapes into two-dimensional cutting patterns. Moreover, modern membrane structures are distinguished from the circus tent and the traditional 'black tent' of the desert nomads by having a surface shape which is doubly curved and prestressed, resulting in greater stability and load-carrying capacity.

For really long span roofs, engineers have invented several tricks. One is that of supporting the membrane on the air contained within the building. This is achieved by raising the internal air pressure by a relatively small amount (up to 100 millimetres of water) above atmospheric. The idea of supporting a roof by air pressure was first put forward by the English engineer F W Lanchester in his patent of 1917 which clearly derived its inspiration from balloons and airships. His own designs were never realised due to the lack of sufficiently durable

Schlumberger Research Centre, Cambridge
Membrane-stress plot
Architect: Michael Hopkins
Engineer (roof): Ove Arup & Partners
© Ove Arup & Partners

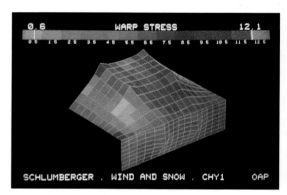

Tokyo 'Big-Egg' Dome, Japan
Architect/engineer: Nikken Sekkei/Takenaka Corp.
© Photograph Nikken Sekkei/Takenaka Corp.

materials and it was not until the 1950s that out of strategic necessity the first air-supported Radomes were built in the United States. These were followed in the 1970s and 1980s by 70,000-seater covered stadiums. The most recent of these is the Tokyo 'Big Egg' Dome of 1988 covering 32,000 square metres.

A second trick exploits the principle of the bicycle wheel by using a radial network of cable beams to provide support to the textile membrane. The cable network is tensioned against a substantial and continuous ring beam. In 1986 the ancient bull ring of Zaragoza was covered with a bicycle wheel, 83 metres in diameter, covered with a PVC-coated polyester membrane. This type of material allows the central part of the roof to be retracted by electric power into a central bunching. However, the outstanding example of the enclosed multipurpose stadium is the oval Georgia Dome in Atlanta with major/minor axes spans of 250 and 180 metres and seating for 70,000 people. The scale, spirit and ingenuity of this and many modern tent structures recall their Roman and Victorian antecedents.

The genetic language of design

John Frazer

The fundamental form-generating processes of nature are currently inspiring artists and designers in fields as diverse as aeronautics, yacht design, architecture, music, fine art and textile design. The traditional inspiration to designers, of the forms and structures of nature, is being replaced by an emphasis on the inner logic and information coding of DNA and the development from a cell to an organism. Only recently have considerable computing power and software innovation made the emulation of the form-generating and evolutionary processes of nature a realistic possibility for designers.

The motivation to approach design in an evolutionary manner varies considerably. In the field of aeronautics, significant improvements in efficiency have been achieved by emulating the refining and honing processes of nature,[1] whilst the interest in art has been in the process and environmentally influenced development of forms.[2] In textile design there are at least two reasons for interest. The first is that weaving and knitting in particular provide a very elegant demonstration and model of an information-coded approach because of the direct correlation between the code and the resulting fabric. The second is that it is possible to evolve very surprising new designs and that the developmental and evolutionary processes are of interest in their own right.

Although nature operates without knowledge of what is to come, that is without design, it is nevertheless tempting to talk of the natural world as having been designed.[3] Given enough time, the blind evolutionary tactics of nature are capable of producing great beauty and complexity by a process of profligate prototyping and ruthless selection: 'Natural selection has superb tactics, but no strategy – but tactics if pursued without thought for the cost and for long enough, can get to places which no strategist would dream of.'[4] In a sense that is how certain craft designs such as Persian rugs, have evolved, but the process is exceptionally slow. The computer now provides a form of evolutionary accelerator where space and time are compressed and countless prototypes can be modelled and evaluated in the imagination of the machine before a single one is produced.

The technique for developing a design from a simple starting point or 'seed' is based on the science of 'cellular automata'.[5] These are simply regular arrays of cells each of which has a state (such as 0 or 1, black or white, alive or dead in the simplest examples). The state of a cell at any moment is dependent not only on its state, but on the states of its neighbours at the previous moment and on transition rules. These rules

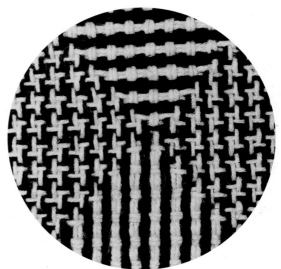

Barbara Dass
Experimental weave samples
Based on a concept of generating weave patterns from weave cells in an analogy with genetics, a series of samples demonstrates the use of symmetry and antisymmetry operations as part of the developmental process.

change the state of a cell, given particular conditions such as if a cell was black and only one of its neighbours was white then make it black. Such a system can produce surprisingly complex results with even the simplest of rules. Weave can be understood as a cellular automata with the state of each crossing, warp over weft or weft over warp, as the state of a cell. Successive rows of the weave are both literally and logically successive states of the automata, so each row of the weave is dependent on the row above and on transition rules.

The technique for evolving a design requires that characteristics are coded in a 'genetic algorithm' which is then subject to very small random mutations.[6] Groups of designs are then developed and the most successful are selected for further development. Selection can be on the basis of the most efficient designs (emulating natural selection) or on aesthetic or other criteria (more comparable to breeding show dogs). For weave this implies again using the crossings of weft over warp, warp over weft as a binary code. This time small mutations or errors in the weave are used to generate new patterns which are then selected or rejected for further development. Just as in nature, by accumulating small changes over a large number of

iterations, surprising new forms can be evolved.[7]

Natural forms develop from a single spherically symmetrical cell to a complex but less symmetrical (bilaterally symmetric in the case of most animals) form, by a process of cell division and progressive symmetry breaking. Symmetry repetitions such as a block repeat are common in textiles although the full range of more complex symmetry operations is rarely appreciated or exploited.[8] But the idea of design development by progressive symmetry breaking also has great potential so far not exploited at all.

These techniques can be combined in weave so that groups of crossings can be understood as letters and then words (permutations of eight crossings give 256 letters and symbols). Thus a row of crossings can be a complex message and set of rules which controls its own development and morphology. The weave is thus the carrier of information and the means of construction, the message in the final row being a development of the seed in the initial row, a fossilised genetic record.

This simplistic model can now be elaborated. The model can first be developed conceptually in the imagination of the designer or the computer and instead of working row by row, we can develop outwards from a seed.[9] The 'letters' of

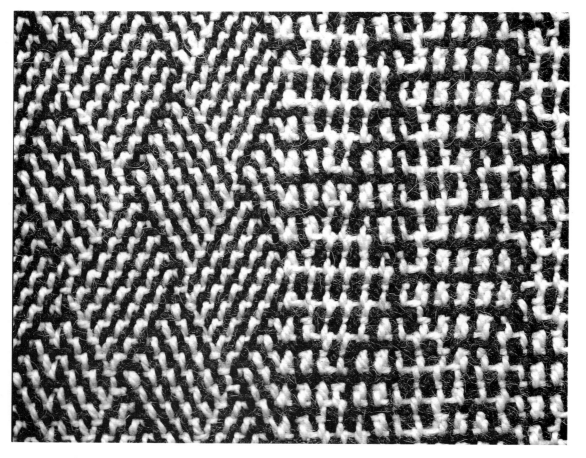

Left and opposite:
Barbara Dass
Experimental weave samples
Weave is understood as information coded in the crossings of weft and warp. The introduction of mutations due to small errors or fault lines is explored as a technique for the progressive evolution of a design.

our genetic language can be not only the binary warp/weft but, by changing the colours, the possible combinations are increased. The 'words' can be combinations of interlacings of weft and warp (or understood operationally as sequences of shaft lifting). The development of the embryonic 'seed' will take place by a series of symmetry repetitions and symmetry-breaking operations. This conceptual model can then be 'evolved' in the computer model by allowing small mutations or errors in the weave, only specific interesting instances being materialized on the loom. These materialisations can form a record of the development of a whole species of weaves all derived from one conceptual seed of an idea in the mind of the designer.

Some of these features are elegantly demonstrated in the weaves of Barbara Dass. There is an explicit analogy with the structure of DNA and her designs are conceived and developed from seeds.[10] She talks of the weave as information of the primary elements of weave cells and she makes extensive use of symmetry operations in the development of the designs. A concept of repressor and operator genes is used to control the conceptual model of the design development.[11] Her most recent work makes extensive use of anti-symmetry

operations and shows the inclusion of abnormal information (genetic mutations).[12] Barbara Dass works both with computers and by manual simulation of the computer processes which is necessary for greater understanding. The illustrations are small experimental samples showing fault lines and symmetry and anti-symmetry development.

With weave the medium always was the message. The data in the pattern is the paternal, intellectual, conceptual data model in the computer and the material is the maternal embodiment of the pattern in the woven fabric. In the case of weave, the data is physically embedded in the structure of the interlacing. Pattern and material are one.

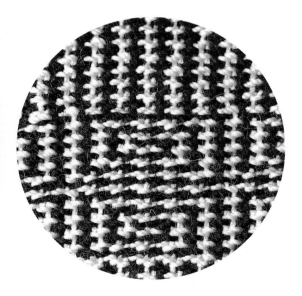

1. See Rechenberg, 'Artificial evolution and artificial intelligence' in Forsyth, R (ed), *Machine Learning*, Chapman & Hall, London 1989.
2. For example Todd, S and Latham, W, *Evolutionary Art and Computers*, Academic Press, 1992.
3. This is the basis of William Paley's famous argument that the existence of something as complex as a watch implied the existence of a watchmaker, and hence that the infinitely greater complexity of nature must imply the existence of a creator. See Paley, W, *Natural Theology*, Oxford 1802.
4. Jones, S, *The Language of the Genes*, Harper Collins, London 1993.
5. Burks, A W, *Essays on Cellular Automata*, University of Illinois, Chicago 1968.

6. Holland, J H, *Adaptation in Natural and Artificial Systems*, University of Michigan Press, Ann Arbor 1975.
7. Frazer, J H, 'Datastructures for Rule-Based and Genetic Design'. In *Visual Computing – Integrating Computer Graphics with Computer Vision*, Springer-Verlag, Tokyo 1992, pp731–744.
8. For a rigorous treatment of symmetry in the plane and in layers see Shubnikov, A V and Koptsik, V A, *Symmetry in Science and Art*, 1972 trans. Plenum Press, New York and London 1974.
9. Frazer, J H and Connor, J M, 'A Conceptual Seeding Technique for Architectural Design', *PArC 79 International Conference on the Application of Computers in Architectural Design*, Proceedings, PArC 79 Online Conferences with AMK, Berlin 1979, pp425–434.

10. Dass, B, *Generative Technique for Weave Design*, DPhil thesis, University of Ulster, 1989.
11. Dass, B, 'Genes and Morphological Relationships in Weave Construction', *Support, Society and Culture – Mutual Uses of Cybernetics and Science*, 1989, Proceedings, University of Amsterdam, pp20–24.
12. Dass, B, 'Metaphorical Weaves: Application of Rules of Anti-symmetry to Weave Design', *Ars Textrina* 19, Winnipeg 1993, pp61–73.

Fabric in fashion

Nilgin Yusuf

Textiles surround and affect us constantly and in every aspect of our lives. From the blanket we are wrapped in at birth to the plush velvet we might be lowered into at death, there is a literal meaning to the phrase 'fabric of life'.

Our most intimate relationship with fabric is that which we wear against our skin. From primitive man's first coarsely stitched together fur pelts, we have always worn clothing for warmth and protection. As our environments and social roles have become more complex, our clothing has adapted to absorb the change. The last hundred years have bought dramatic changes to our lives. Industrialisation, jet travel, air conditioning and central heating are just some of the factors that have played key roles in the ever-changing world of clothing. It is now possible to travel to dramatically different climates. We no longer need to wear thick, heavy garments; the world has become a warmer place, inside and out. Contemporary clothing is lighter than ever before and easier, with the emphasis on thin layers rather than bulk.

Comfort is the prerequisite of clothing today. Clothes which stretch and mould with the natural form rather than imposing a rigid, unyielding shell, have become the norm. Lycra, the wonder fibre that came to prominence in the 1980s, liberated a generation of women and revolutionised the fashion world. It is arguable that fabrics rather than shapes move fashion on. Did Coco Chanel's little suit become a modern classic because of its shape – or because of the jersey in which it was fashioned? Some designers, including the American Geoffrey Beene, believe it was the lightweight, easy jersey, previously used for undergarments, not the jacket, that was truly radical and fitting to the modern woman.

It is the fashion designer's job to dress the needs of modern living – to make life in the ever-changing, complex, modern world as comfortable and easy as possible. As many fashion designers chase one silhouette after the other, and the historical prototypes are dredged up for stylistic reference, those few designers who understand the importance of fabric are proving themselves to be on the cutting edge. Long or short, grunge or glam, A-line or bustle back, all fade into stylistic oblivion when compared to the fabric manipulators. While the stylists skit along the surface, the conceptualists dare to push the boundaries of fashion by either inventing fabrics of their own, or bringing unexpected textile concepts to the world of fashion. This is clothing design from the inside out that is questioning, challenging and provocative.

'The future of fashion will come from the laboratory, not a sketch pad', according to Geoffrey Beene. This is increasingly the case and in the twenty-first century, one imagines that the fashion designer's job will be that of scientist as well as aesthete. Issey Miyake plays a starring role in fashion modernism. In his textile studio in Tokyo, headed by Makiko Minagawa, he constantly strives to create new, exciting fabrics. Using anything from aluminium to paper or grass, materials are heated or treated to create some of the most visually exciting fabrics in the fashion world. Miyake's pleats, a contemporary classic, may look fragile, delicate even poetic, but they stand up well to the rigours of contemporary life and can be machine-washed. Miyake's catwalk shows are an artistic *tour de force*; his originality and passion for design leaves the spectator dazzled.

Charles and Patricia Lester, based in Abergavenny, South Wales, earned their reputation for beautifully sinuous, finely-pleated dresses. Many compared their work to that of the Venetian designer Mariano Fortuny, whose turn-of-the-century work was inspired by sixteenth-century tapestries. More recently their work has diversified to incorporate richly coloured and patterned velvets. Their experimentation explores visual, aesthetic and sensual routes that combine history with modernity. They explain: 'We invent techniques for decorating textiles.

i Kawakubo for Comme
s Garçons
ack dress, bonded cotton
yon and polyurethane
tumn/winter 1986-87
i Kawakubo is the Japanese
signer behind the name
mme des Garçons. She has
rked closely with textile
signers and is very interested
the fabric structure. This
ess is made of a bonded
tton, rayon and
lyurethane. The fabric is
ulptural and capable of
lding shape yet retains
xibility and softness.
Photograph Steven Meisel,
86

Issey Miyake
Autumn 1994 collection
© *Photograph Chris Moore*

Helmut Lang
Autumn/winter 1994 collection
© *Photograph Chris Moore*

Left:
Romeo Gigli
Coat, cotton and velvet painted
and heat embossed with
polyurethane
Autumn/winter 1989/90
© *Collection Italia*
Opposite:
Nigel Atkinson
'King Lear Leaf', 1994
Crèpe satin

Misting, for instance, involves taking the bloom off velvet. We treat silk to give it the feel of suede and make it look bruised. We use modern approaches to re-invent textures from the past.' Their approach to fabric offers a richness and sensuality that had until relatively recently been outlawed by the modernists and purists. Their work is also reminiscent of the beautifully hand-crafted fabrics produced by the Arts and Crafts movement in the late nineteenth century. But it is chemicals and treatments and long hours in a laboratory that make many of these techniques possible and practical.

Another pioneer, Nigel Atkinson, graduated from the Royal College of Art in London in the late eighties and gained almost instant notoriety for cooking his fabrics. Soon after graduation, he was commissioned by Romeo Gigli to create a range of fantastically rich, pleated velvets. Since then he has been experimenting, devising new decorative and structural techniques for use in fashion and interiors. He explains: 'I use printing as a way of changing the nature of the cloth. Rather than using print as a way of applying two-dimensional images, I affect the fabric in a much more three-dimensional way. I also like to create ambiguities of age, producing hand-made fabrics which don't necessarily look new. Fabrics might look like suede or leather but are actually silk

with polyurethane.' Other designers, including Helmut Lang and Alexander McQueen, are also using fabrics and materials to give new expression to their collections.

In art schools, an increasing number of fashion students are experimenting with fabric. They are developing the confidence to manipulate and experiment with it, to distress, bleach, and boil it. Hussein Chalayan, a recent graduate from Central St Martin's College of Art and Design, has recently gained much press from the fact that he buried his fabric to see how it would disintegrate and distress. Though some of the ideas might seem frankly daft, and some designs look more perplexing than tantalising on the catwalks, there is a growing realisation that fabric holds the key to fashion's future. It is the designer's job to unlock it.

Creating creating

Stewart Brand

Who gains more from the symbiosis of art and new media, the voracious artists or the perpetually emerging media?

For the artist, diving into a new medium is a triple shortcut; one to a novelty; two, to mastery; three, to the frontier of cognition.

Increasingly, over the last century or so, originality has been a prime goal of artists; preferably lifelong originality, where you're continually surprising your audience and ideally yourself. If you're among the first into electronic music, adventure computer games, virtual reality, or artificial life, you get a free ride on the novelty of the medium. There's no tradition to overcome. Invention is already manifest in the medium. All you have to do is play, and it looks like invention. Often it is.

There are also no previous masters to equal or surpass. After only a few weeks of delving, you're the master. (Try doing that with a violin.) The medium might even become synonymous with your name for a while.

And you're not Thoreau exploring some pond. You're Cabeza de Vaca exploring a continent, freed to magic by your circumstances, with discovery waiting in every direction. And it's discovery not just for you; you're exploring for all humankind. The cutting edge of new media is the cutting edge of human cognition, which is the edge of what it means to be human.

You get to inhabit a new version of the parable of oil paint in tubes. Painters once prepared and mixed their own oil paints. Then pre-mixed oil paint in metal tubes was invented. It didn't seem like a major advance in technology, but suddenly a generation of French painters could leave their studios and go outside and squeeze paint on the palette like toothpaste. Their joy of release – both in subject and medium – we know as French Impressionism.

This is sounding like one of those motiviational speeches that I usually refuse to give. One time, though, I was offered such a handsome fee that I agreed to speak to a sales representatives' and buyers' retreat for Prime Computer on a Caribbean island. Prime makes minicomputers. This was about 1985. I was supposed to deliver a rave-up about the joys and boundless future of computing. Instead, I said that just as minicomputers had put mainframe manufacturers out of business, personal computers were about to do the same thing to minicomputer manufacturers, and I asked what Prime was going to do about that.

Here's what they did about it. They complained about the speech to my speaker's bureau, which dropped me. And Prime went Chapter 11 last year.

So – to keep my Cassandra string going – who's going to put new media artists out of business? The process itself. All that 'cutting edge' business cuts both ways – it's a knife that's all blade, no handle. You may master a lovely new media continent, but there's always another, and your investment in the present means you'll probably miss the next one. Soon you're a has-been at 24. Maybe you can get work doing ads, but you had better hurry.

It's the paradox of novelty; nothing gets old faster. Quick win, quick lose. Some people do art for immortality. You have to give that up if you're going to work in cutting-edge new media. Everything is written on the wind. As we say of the Electronic Frontier Foundation's newsletter, 'Printed on 100 per cent recycled electrons.'

Never mind the artist's ego and career, what about art itself? How does a culture get any aesthetic, grounding or continuity from art forms with the longevity of mayflies? Does anything lasting escape from the black hole of accelerating technology?

As a young artist, I would have had a quick answer: 'Hey, the metamessage is change. That's what it's all about.' Ooo, profound. To claim that the crippling limitation of one's art is its real message is pretty pathetic.

These are serious questions. Has technology swallowed art, and so is art gone now? Or are we so inside technology that from here it's all art? Or is that confusing art with artifice?

The art I care about is usually at guerrilla war with artifice, employing and subverting the artificial to reawaken the real – jack back out into 'the total animal soup of time'. (I think that's Allen Ginsberg.) We keep making more and more splendid mirrors with these sophisticated technologies. I remember something I saw scribbled on a whiteboard at the Media Lab at the Massachusetts Institute of Technology: 'Art is not a mirror. Art is a hammer'.

Enough about art. What about media? What does it gain from the cyber-artistic symbiosis? When I worked at the Media Lab the deal was very clear. The Lab was not there for the artists. The artists were there for the Lab. Their job was to supplement the scientists and engineers in three important ways:
– They were to be cognitive pioneers.
– They were to ensure that all demos were done with art – that is, presentational craft.
– And they were to keep things culturally innovative. Having real artists around was supposed to infect the place with quality, which it did.
Inventors often loose interest in a nifty new concept once it is proven. Artists are perfect to

pick up the ball at that point. The white-light holograms you see on your credit cards were invented by Steve Benton when he worked at Polaroid. Some New York artists begged the original technique from him and proceed to push it – and him – towards something really dazzling. They opened a holography museum in New York and eventually they got enough publicity so that holograms wound up on the cover of *National Geographic*, on toys, and on money.

White light holograms are now a mini-industry. Those original hologram art pieces in New York, and the artists, are long forgotten.

What is the lesson? It looks like 'media wins, artists lose'. All high-tech art becomes effectively anonymous and ephemeral. As an artist you might as well be a Gothic cathedral sculptor, honoured for your very namelessness, or a Navaho sand-painter, admired and forgotten along with your fleeting work.

Have any new-media works escaped the black hole of accelerating technology? I can think of two. If you go to the Computer Museum in Boson you will find a huge minicomputer so ancient it has a round screen.

This is the original Digital Equipment PDP-1, from 1961 or so. The machine is up and working. On the screen you can see tiny spaceships dashing around. The machine is playing the original 'Space War', devised by Steve Russell and half-a-dozen hacker friends. That game was so brilliant and addictive, it swept through all the computer labs in the world in a matter of weeks. In many respects, 'Space War' has still not been surpassed even 50 years later.

Another survivor dates from 1978 and also came out of MIT. This was the *Aspen Movie Map* – a computerised way to drive around Aspen, Colorado, in space and time via an enhanced videodisk. It was done by people at Nicholas Negroponte's Architecture Machine Group. The *Aspen Movie Map* was one of those landmark demos that got around to all the conferences and inspired a generation of innovators and artists – in this case about multimedia where the user of the work becomes the author.

These examples have several things in common. For one, they were highly collaborative. Two, they pushed a new technology beyond what anyone imagined possible into something dramatic, whole, and full of promise. Three, they were, fundamentally, not works, but tools. 'Space War' was a game, nothing without players, and never the same from game to game. The *Aspen Movie Map* was not a tour of Aspen; it was Aspen. The tour was what you did with it.

In each case, new media were inspired into existence. Computer games and interactive multimedia are whole worlds that came out of those generative moments, and worlds sometimes remember their origins.

Creating in new media always has that deeper possibility. You might be creating a medium itself. You might be creating creating. That's worth risking anonymity for.

This piece was the keynote speech at the 1992 CyberArts Conference in Pasadena, California. Reproduced by kind permission of Wired *magazine.*

Tactile texts

Renata Brink

To simulate: To reproduce the conditions (of a situation etc.) as in carrying out an experiment. To assume or to have the appearance of, to imitate.

Simulacrum: From Lat. likeness, from simulare; to imitate, from similis: like. Any image or representation of s.th.[1]

This text will attempt to interweave and discuss three aspects which to me seem relevant within the context of representation of computer-generated or computer-influenced textiles.
- The 'texts' of the textiles: what signs are produced by this fusion of high tech and material?
- Is there a change of content through the availability of electronic media?
- I will argue that computers and simulation generate a challenging desire for 'Stofflichkeit', matter, i.e. material in relation to textiles. Is matter material?

Computers are adding a new complex language within the sphere of textiles: difference and plurality in producing meaning are generated through digits and an infinite chain of yes/no and either/or choices, coded and decoded in abstract ideas of time and space: lightspeed and electronic chip. Endless combinations are possible through the grid of these two principles which are neither binary in semiotic terms nor a dichotomy: their seeming oppositions are dissolved into sheer endlessness and ability to produce detail.

Differentiation in both structure and image opens up possibilities of wider contexts of imagery and signs, and is bringing textiles directly into the discourse of representation. The horizon of play and the thin line between being overwhelmed by or surrendering to high technology is generating rich tensions and challenges.[2] By scanning these very possibilities textiles are expanding their texts into illusion, trompe-l'oeil, parody, play, reference and quotation and consequently to multi-layered structures of content.

The computer is extending boundaries in the use of images and signs. The screen as an electronic, visual information membrane in relation to fabric and fibre is proposing its transcendence into material, creating a rupture, a fissure between a switch and a tactile, textured object. The images and signs (I include structure in my use of the terms), whether 'carried' within the structures or produced through use of a computer, are allowing fabrics into the realm of the present rather than the past. (Textiles were previously thought of as a 'slow' medium in art , having domestic connotations in industrial manufacturing.)

The electronic 'curtain' of visual information on the screen anticipates any further transformation. Its seductive images and hypnotic qualities are creating their own 'demand', their own desires within the material, longing to unfold themselves.

The inherent qualities in textiles of fragility and their lack of durability can strongly contradict sterility, perfection and slickness without mystery. However, paradoxes remain between the material and the electronic fabric.

The computer is another medium in the chain of transcriptions transcribing images and a pool of signs (including structures) which are leaving their imprints on the textiles themselves. Through the scanning of images and objects and the laser 'touch' reading the information and projecting its textured surface like a skin back onto the screen ready for manipulation, the everyday maybe included in textiles, themselves often regarded as domestic, ordinary, speechless, passive covers.

Their appearance as an electrical 'body' is virtually 'fabricated', or shaped prior to being made into tactile and soft surfaces.

Through the gap between simulation and production a further space is being opened up, in which textiles can be self-referential or critical in the same way that paintings or sculptures can speak about themselves. The materials as an entity distinct from the canvas is not subordinated to meaning but has its own material importance, with a close relationship to its content.

Are computer-generated textiles not an embodiment of simulated ideas through the screen and the printer into substance? Materialised (into) material?

Matter and subject matter are interwoven and images and structural orders brought into corporeality. Multiple layers of meaning through a language of fibre more expanded, more differentiated and enriched, where structure, colour, material and images form a complex sign-context, both narrative and non-narrative (including the respective haptic qualities and the whole domain of the sensuous) thus contribute to contemporary debates of image and sign within the 'weak' fibre context with the circulation of more differentiated signs.

For the transformation of signs drawn, photographed, found, i.e. the use of signs in textiles as quotations, the computer is a connection, simulating the idea of material – textiles are a possible material form of the electronic images where the material takes on qualities of shifting imagery in its pliability, stretchability and expansion of surface. The higher the resolution of the technical options, the more refined is the immediate or transformative potential within the subject matter.

The electronic media and their dotted data, their fragments of visual information, stored in the (micro) chip entertain a close relationship with textiles. I suggest that the dialogue works both ways: the concept of fibre as units to be crossed (in weaving), looped (in knitting) is scanned. The electronic grids, with their raised networks transferring information onto and across the material, the passing evanescence of screen 'lights' and the electronic weave and textiles in time, I suggest, entertain a kinship or a similarity in their mutual qualities of units, digits, repeats, and electronic textuality.

If the notion of text is expanded into any sign context (not necessarily verbal or visual), the text of the order for CAM or the text of the image for CAD are in close textual proximity to the text of textiles *per se*, whose tactile quality is simulated in its material existence, and whose sensual properties are stored in the compressed chip-information unfolding into the fabric.

These different processes are generated by desire. The screen is at first a visual matrix, as ephemeral as the textile to be made and as

'virtual' as the very gap creating the desire for material substance. Sensual processes like draping, folding, wrapping and hanging, however well these are being simulated outside textiles, leave open this gap – the space where soft and shapable textile material can be thought and where the morphology of fabric remains the desired materiality.

Textiles and their properties and peculiarities are expanding and stretching their domains of use and of thought.

1. After the *Collins Concise English Dictionary*, 1989.
2. Idea borrowed from Jean Baudrillard, 'On Seduction', in Poster, Mark (ed.), *Selected Writing* , Stanford University Press, 1988.

Bibliography

Respect for tradition, curiosity for technology

Books

The International Design Yearbooks:
1988–89 (ed. Arata Isozaki)
1989–90 (ed. Oscar Tusquets Blanca)
1990–91 (ed. Mario Bellini)
1992 (ed. Andrée Putmann)
all published by Thames and Hudson, London,
and 1993 (ed. Borek Sipek) published by Laurence King, London

Colchester, Chloë, *The New Textiles*, Thames and Hudson, London 1991

Manzini, Enzio, *The Material of Invention*, MIT Press, Cambridge, Massachusetts 1989

Sudjic, Deyan, *Rei Kawakubo and Comme des Garçons*, Fourth Estate, London 1990

Catalogues

Hand and Technology – Textile by Junichi Arai, Japan 1992

Makiko Minagawa: Fabric, Gallery Ma, Tokyo 1990

Issey Miyake – Ten Sen Men, City Museum of Contemporary Art, Hiroshima 1990

Articles

Cocks, Jay, 'A Change of Clothes' (Issey Miyake), *Time*, 27 January 1986

Davies, Stephen, 'Silk-like Breathable and Other Microfilament Fabrics', *Textile Outlook International*, January 1990

Frei, Helena, 'Junichi Arai: a Designer's Use of Visual and Textural Contrasts', *Fiber Arts*, USA, Summer 1992

Holborn, Mark, 'Image of a Second Skin', *Artforum*, November 1988

Koplos, Janet, 'Spirited Away: the Japanese Folkcraft Tradition', *Crafts*, September/October 1989

Louie, Elaine, 'New Era in Design Materials', *The New York Times*, 19 August 1993

Nakamuru, Hisao, President of Kuraray, *Kuraray Corporate Profile*, Japan 1992

Smith, Roberta, 'A Weaving of Stainless-Steel Thread', *The New York Times*, 10 May 1991

Sudo, Reiko, 'Von Textildesign zu Architextil', *Textilforum*, Germany January 1992

Yee, Roger, 'Weaving in Bark And Steel', *Contract Design*, August 1992

Yusuf, Nilgin, 'Fabric of Life', *Elle* (UK edition), October 1991

Yusuf, Nilgin, 'Issey Miyake – Ancient Tradition and Bold Futurism', *Vogue* (UK edition), June 1992

'The Development of New Fibres with Sophisticated Functions as High Added-Value Products', *Knitting International*, June 1992

Mainichi Daily News (Junichi Arai), 27 February 1989

Scanning the inner fabric

Books

Baker, Robin, *Designing the Future*, Thames & Hudson, London 1993

Master Weavers: Tapestry from the Dovecot Studios 1912–1980 Cannongate Publishing, Edinburgh 1980

McCorduck, Pamela, *Aaron's Code*, Freeman Publications, 1991

Articles

Gray, Stephen, 'The Computerised Catwalk' *Textile Horizons*, June 1993

Hearle, John W S, 'Can fabric hand enter the dataspace?' *Textile Horizons*; April 1993

Hearle, John W S, 'Computer-Aided Textile Design' *Textile Horizons*; October 1993

Holme, Ian, 'Design '89: Computer Aided Design', *Knitting International*, June 1989

Holme, Ian, 'Revolution under way in textile design' *Textile Month*, June 1989

Reports & Catalogues

Corwin, Mary, *Cynthia Schira – New York*, Spencer Museum of Art, University of Kansas, Kansas; May 1987 exhibition catalogue

Fozzard, G J W and Rawling, A J, 'CAD for Garment Design: Effective use of the Third Dimension, *Proceedings of the 8th National Conference for Manufacturing Research*

Gray, Stephen, *Making it Work – Computer Aided Design & Manafacturing II*, Design Council, London 1993

Müller-Zell, *Art & Industry* (Cynthia Schira), exhibition catalogue for show at the Museum für Industriekulfür, Nürnberg, August 1991

Across the divide

Books

Collins, Michael *Tom Dixon*, Phaidon, London 1990

Davies, Colin *Hopkins – The Work of Michael Hopkins & Partners*, Phaidon, London 1993

Jenkins, David *Lord's Cricket Ground, London 1987*, Phaidon, London 1991

Jenkins, David *Schlumberger Cambridge Research Centre, Cambridge 1985*, Phaidon;, London 1993

Lyall, Sutherland *Imagination Headquarters, London 1990*, Phaidon, London 1992

Pawley, Martin *Future Systems, the Story of Tomorrow*, Phaidon, London 1993

Articles

'Roof Grandstand' (Goodwood polyester reinforced PVC roof), *The Architects' Journal*, 26 February 1992

'Tent Structures – are they architecture?' *Architectural Record*, May 1980

'The Era of Swoops & Billows', *Progressive Architecture*, June 1980

Reports & Catalogues

Exploring Materials: The Work of Peter Rice, Ove Arup Associates, London 1992

The alchemist's art

Books

Davis, Mike, *City of Quartz*, Verso Press, London 1990

Gibson, William, *Neuromancer*, Ace Science Fiction, New York 1984

Hofstadter, Douglas R Godel, *Escher, Bach: An Eternal Golden Braid – a metaphorical fugue on minds and machines in the spirit of Lewis Carroll*,

Penguin Books, London 1986 Levy, Steven, *Artificial Life – the quest for a new creation*, Penguin Books, London 1993

MacKenzie, Dorothy, *Green Design – Design for the Environment*, Laurence King, London 1991

McLuhan, Marshall, *Understanding Media*, McGraw-Hill, New York 1964

Pawley, Martin, *Theory and Design in the Second Machine Age*, Basil Blackwell, London 1990

Vanlaethem, France, *Gaetano Pesce* Thames & Hudson, London 1989

Yelavich, Susan, *The Edge of the Millenium – an international critique of architecture, urban planning, product and communication design*, Whitney Library of Design, New York 1993

Articles

Battle, Guy and McCarthy, Christopher, 'Multi-Source Synthesis – A future engineering response to climatic forces in architecture' *Architectural Design Magazine*, July/August 1993

Edwards, Mark, 'It's the thought that counts – have computers usurped our ability to think?', *The Sunday Times*, London, 1 August 1993

Margolis, Jonathan, 'Wall to Wall Intellect' *The Sunday Times*, London, 15 August 1994

Taylor, Sean, 'What goes around comes around' (the fashion industry and the environment), *The Guardian*; 17 August 1992

'Textiles and the Environment', *Textile Horizons*, October 1992 (series of articles)

Reports & Catalogues

Culshaw, B, Gardiner, P T and McDonach, A (eds.), *First European Conference on Smart Structures and Materials SPIE*, Volume 1777, Europto Series, Institute of Physics Publishing, Bristol and Philadelphia and EOS/SPIE, May 1992

Minale, Tattersfield & Partners *Textile View*, 'Felt: a link with the past, a key to the future', Mantero Seta SpA, Italy, August 1992

Minale, Tattersfield & Partners *Textile View*: 'Silk, Satin, Cotton, Rags: just add Plastic', Mantero Seta SpA; Italy, March 1992

Smart Materials & Structures (report on a DTI Overseas Science & Technology Expert Mission to Japan), Institute of Materials, London 1994

'The New Alchemists', transcript from BBC Horizon programme transmitted on 19, April 1993

General

Books

Colchester, Chloë, *The New Textiles*, Thames and Hudson, London 1991

Cook, Peter and Llewellyn Jones, Rosie, *New Spirit in Architecture*, Rizzoli, New York 1991

Itsuko Hasegawa, Academy Editions, London 1993

Hugues, Patrice, 'Le Langage du Tissu', *Textile/Art/Langage*, Paris 1982

Margetts, Martina, (ed.), *International Crafts*, Thames & Hudson, London 1991

Popper, Frank, *Art of the Electronic Age*, Thames & Hudson, London 1993

van Raay, Stefan, (ed.), 'Imitation and Inspiration: The Japanese Influence on Dutch Art' (article on Maria Blaisse), *Art Unlimited*, Amsterdam 1989

Catalogues

Seven Illusions (Vibeke Riisberg), Stenlasen, 1993

15th Biennale Internationale de la Tapisserie, Lausanne 1992

European Influences, Crafts Council, London 1992

International Triennale of Tapestry, Central Museum of Textiles, Lodz 1992

Issey Miyake, Musée des Arts Décoratifs, Paris 1988

Jacquard – Project, Art & Industrie, Museum für Industriekultur, Nürnberg 1991

Kyoko Kumai, The Museum of Modern Art, New York 1991

Living Design from Denmark (Vibeke Riisberg, exhibitor), Baltic Countries 1992

The Power of Softness (Maria Blaisse, exhibitor), Stedelijk Museum, Amsterdam 1989

Articles

Bates, Angi, 'Dream Weaves', *Interiors*, June 1991

Blanchard, Tamsin, 'Now Available in Paperback', *The Independent*, 12 February 1994

Buckett, Debbie, 'A New Diet of High Fibres', *The Guardian*, 25 February 1993

DuBois, Emily, 'Swatches', *Fiberarts*, March/April 1992

Holorn, Mark, 'Image of a Second Skin', *Artforum*, November 1988

Hume, Marion, 'Japan Ease', *The Independent on Sunday*, 13 June 1993

Patel, A. Jini, 'Designer Creates Unique Blend' *The Japan Times*, 10 May 1990

Endlich, Donna Larsen and Seventy, Sylvia, 'Transforming Textiles' (article includes Emily DuBois), *Fiberarts*, January/February 1992

Nutt, John, 'The Australian Practice', *The Arup Journal*, London, October 1986

Spencer, Mimi, 'Arts and the Man … (Issey Miyake), *Vogue* (UK edition), July 1993

Sterk, Beatrijs, 'Kunst & Industrie', *Textilforum*, March 1991

Vollrath, Fritz, 'Spiders Web and Silks', *Scientific American*, 1992

Yusuf, Nilgin, 'The Future of Fashion', *Marie Claire (UK edition)*, November 1992

Zelinsky, Marilyn, 'Breaking New Ground', *Interiors*, March 1992

'Centro Richerche Mantero', *Textile View*, Summer 1992

First published 1994 by
Artemis London Limited,
55 Charlotte Road,
London EC2A 3QT

British Library Cataloguing
in Publication
A CIP record for this book is
available from the British Library

ISBN 1 874056 08 0 (London)
ISBN 3 7608 8434 2 (Zürich)

Designed by Stephen Coates
Repro by Precise, London
Printed by Smart Arts, Brighton

This publication is funded by the
Crafts Council to accompany the
exhibition 2010, curated by Sarah
Braddock and Marie O'Mahony at
the Crafts Council Gallery, London
(15 September - 13 November
1994), followed by a UK and
European tour.

Acknowledgements
We would like to acknowledge the
Arts Council of England, the Office of
Science & Technology and Goldsmiths
College, University of London. who have
proved invaluable in their support
towards the research and development
of the 2010 exhibition and this book.
Thanks to Wired magazine for kindly
allowing us to reprint Stewart Brand's
essay 'Creating Creating' which was
first published in their premier issue.
Special thanks to all those who have
contributed to and supported this book.

Cover photograph:
Junichi Arai
'Big Checkerboard', 1985
100 per cent nylon
© Nuno Corporation
Photograph by Anthony Oliver